IT AIN'T JUST THE DIET™
FOOD JOURNAL
A Daily Guide to Finding & Managing Your Food Allergies

IT AIN'T JUST THE DIET™
FOOD JOURNAL

A Daily Guide to Finding & Managing Your Food Allergies
Lois Carter Crawford

Marketing Idea Shop, LLC
Harrisonburg, Virginia | United States

IT AIN'T JUST THE DIET™
FOOD JOURNAL
A Daily Guide to Finding & Managing Your Food Allergies

Lois Carter Crawford

Published by:
Recipe Idea Shop, a brand of
Marketing Idea Shop, LLC
Harrisonburg, Virginia 22802 / USA
Email: Lois@RecipeIdeaShop.com

Affiliated Websites:
RecipeIdeaShop.com
MarketingIdeaShop.com
SofterSideOfSelling.com

Author photos by Swartz Photography, Harrisonburg, Virginia.
Cover photo by Olia Nayda via Unsplash.
All other photos © Marketing Idea Shop, LLC.
Editing by Anjuli Rose Editorial, Seattle, Washington.

Printed in the United States of America.

Disclaimer:
The author is not a health professional or nutritionist. She is offering her research and personal reflections about her health journey and is not providing any type of medical or nutritional advice.

This book is for information purposes only. It is offered as a tool for people to discover their own suspected food allergies, intolerances and sensitivities. Readers are highly encouraged to read, write and reflect on the ideas presented. Consult your healthcare professional before initiating any dietary or exercise program.

Published April 2021

ISBN-978-0-9742511-7-2

IT AIN'T JUST THE DIET™
BEAT FOOD ALLERGIES
ONE BITE AT A TIME

Thank you to my daughter, Erin Fay, for loving me and providing advice. And thanks to my husband, Don Crawford, for helping me with creative ideas, taste testing all my recipes, and being supportive throughout my healing process. Finally, thank you to my coach, Trish Lindemood, for all her help and ideas.

CONTENTS

Initial Journal Prompt:
What concerns about food allergies and intolerances do you have?
Why and how do you plan to use this food journal?

_____

_____

_____

_____

_____

_____

_____

_____

_____

_____

_____

_____

_____

_____

_____

_____

_____

_____

_____

_____

_____

_____

_____

_____

_____

_____

_____

_____

_____

_____

_____

_____

_____

_____

_____

_____

INTRODUCTION
It Ain't Just the Diet

> *"When I was eating gluten,*
> *dairy and soy, I believe my body*
> *thought I was starving. It held*
> *onto all the weight it could."*
> ~ *Lois Carter Crawford*
> *(American Author and Recipe Developer)*

Trial and Painful Error

A few years ago I discovered many of my chronic health issues—including a moderate heart attack and a slow-and-steady weight gain of more than 60 pounds—were caused by my body's reaction to the food I was giving it.

Instead of nourishing my body, *my food was making me sick.*

Thankfully, I learned what to do to change that downward spiral. I am now healthy, and I believe I healed myself with food by tackling my food-related problems. I got rid of the constant pain, and I lost more than 40 pounds without ever "dieting."

The weight just slipped off and stayed off.

Help is Here

Since you are reading this book, I'd guess you suspect that a food allergy, sensitivity, or intolerance is causing a problem for you or someone you love. Well, you've come to the right place.

If you use this *It Ain't Just the Diet Food Journal* to record your food and symptoms, I believe you can discover what foods are surreptitiously wreaking havoc in your body. When you see how good you feel without them, you can make different choices and feel better.

What I Learned

I suffered with pain, bloating, an unpredictable bowel movement pattern, foggy brain, hot flashes, and so much more before I became methodical in writing down what I was eating and what corresponding symptoms I had. When I understood what was causing the problems, I began to heal.

I *wish* I could eat whatever I want and not suffer pain or digestive issues. But I can't. In fact, some foods, such as soy milk, cheese, and gluten, cause severe problems for me when I eat them.

My reaction to soy milk is immediate and severe, indicating an *allergy*. Cheese takes a little longer—about an hour—*but it lasts almost a week*. Gluten, on the other hand, is sneaky. It waits to cause me trouble for three or more days until I forget what I ate, and I am completely baffled when I have to spend half a day in the bathroom.

Is that you, too? I'm so glad I found a solution and developed a daily food tracking form that works brilliantly for me. I want to help you, too, and I share my form with you in this food journal. But first, let's start with a few basics about food allergies.

CHAPTER 1

1

How to Identify Food Allergies, Sensitivities & Intolerances

"What happens when the world is your oyster and you are allergic to shellfish?"
~ Neil Leckman (American Author)

Why Are Food Allergies Increasing?
Do you know that food allergies in the U.S. are on the rise, and these allergies often start in adulthood?[1] It's not just a crazy diet trend or something your brain tricked you into thinking. It's real.

There are many theories about why allergies are increasing. I don't know the answer, but according to Dr. Terry Wahls, author of *The Wahls Protocol,* some of the possibilities are:

- We were made to be hunter-gatherers, and now we are eat-for-convenience people.
- The foods we eat are not local or picked the same day.
- Current foods have fewer natural nutrients.
- We don't eat a variety of foods and colors.
- More food is genetically engineered to produce a high yield instead of nutrition.
- More chemicals are sprayed on growing food.[2]

And *it ain't just the diet* that's causing you to gain weight or suffer food-related problems. You can follow any diet you choose and still not lose weight or stop the pounds from coming back.

What's the Difference Between Food Allergies, Sensitivities & Intolerances?

Why are some symptoms clear and severe? And others take you ages to figure out? The body reacts differently depending on whether you are actually allergic to something, have an intolerance, or are merely sensitive to a food.[3] Let me explain the difference.

Allergies prompt your immune system to go into high alert.

As someone who gets sick from some foods, I pay closer attention to avoiding the one food (soy milk) that gives me an immediate, hyper-response than I do to other food issues. The reaction I had one time was enough to make me say, "Never again!"

If you have that kind of reaction—one that makes you take medicine, such as an antihistamine to control your symptoms, or requires a trip to the hospital—that's an allergy.

Food sensitivities also involve the immune system, but the symptoms are delayed and often harder to figure out. After eating, you may be sleepy or unable to think. Or you may have a wide variety of problems, and you simply can't identify the source(s).

I get foggy brained. My joints hurt and my skin becomes hypersensitive. My mother had trouble with eczema. Some people get acne, headaches, bad breath, gas and bloating, or stinky feet. Others become anxious, aggressive, hyperactive, or depressed. And, of course, these are only some of the ways a body reacts.

Food intolerances do not directly involve your immune system. That is, your immune system doesn't act as if you have been invaded by a virus or bacteria.

With a food intolerance—for instance, lactose intolerance— *only* the digestive system is involved, with all your problems happening in the digestive tract. You are unable to properly digest a food without problems. It may go through your system wholly undigested or induce an inflammatory response only in your digestive tract, causing gas, pain, constipation, and/or diarrhea.

What Are the Most Common Food Culprits?

There are many foods that can cause myriad reactions in people who are allergic, sensitive, or intolerant to them. Sometimes the response is immediate, which suggests you are allergic to it. Sometimes you have a delayed response which can last from ten minutes to up to six days, according to Dr. Doris Rapp, M.D., noted allergy expert and author of *Is This Your Child? Discovering Unrecognized Allergies in Children and Adults.*[4]

In a fact sheet compiled by FARE (Food Allergy Research and Education), we learn:

"More than 170 foods have been reported to cause reactions in the U.S. Eight major food allergens—milk, egg, peanut, tree nuts, wheat, soy, fish and crustacean shellfish—are responsible for most of the serious food allergy reactions in the United States. The most common food allergies in children are allergies to peanut, milk, shellfish and tree nut."[5]

There are, of course, other common foods that cause problems. They are (in alphabetical order):

- Citrus
- Coffee
- Corn
- Dairy
- Eggs
- Fish
- Gluten (wheat)

- Meat (beef, lamb, pork)
- Peanuts
- Raw fruits & vegetables
- Sesame
- Shellfish
- Soy
- Tree nuts[6]

Dr. Rapp identified many other foods and products that caused reactions in her patients, namely:

- Apples
- Avocados
- Bananas
- Beans
- Bell peppers
- Cinnamon
- Chocolate
- Cocoa
- Cola
- Eggplant
- Food additives, dyes, or preservatives
- Garlic
- Grains (other than wheat)
- Grapes
- Mangoes
- Onions
- Oranges
- Peas
- Peanut butter
- Pineapples
- Potatoes
- Sugar
- Sulfites (found in red wine & processed meat)
- Tea
- Tomatoes
- Yeast

Food Reactions & Medical Signs of Issues
A variety of medical problems, such as hyperactivity, ear infections, muscle pain or weakness, joint tightness, asthma, headaches, recurrent infections, and more, can actually be symptoms of food allergies.[8]

Some immediate—and more serious—signs and symptoms of a food allergy might include:

- Anaphylactic shock
- Itching of eyes or face
- Varying degrees of swelling of the mouth, throat, & tongue that can make breathing & swallowing difficult
- Hives
- Abdominal pain
- Cramps
- Vomiting
- Diarrhea
- Mental confusion or dizziness[9]

But what if you simply have to clear your throat frequently? Or you feel bloated after eating? Are these food reactions? They can be.

In fact, you may experience *many* symptoms that you do not recognize as food allergies or sensitivities. Some include:
- Skin problems, like eczema, acne, odd bumps, itchy skin, or ticklishness
- Sinus and hay fever problems, asthma, and other respiratory issues
- Bags, wrinkles, or circles under the eyes (may be dark)
- Red ears and/or bright red cheeks, which are not related to being hot or sunburned
- Constant runny noses (and wiping it upward in kind of a "salute"), sometimes causing a semi-permanent or permanent wrinkle across the bridge of the nose
- Chronic ear or throat infections
- Unproductive coughing, sneezing, or clearing the throat
- Muscle aches
- Foggy brain or trouble remembering or thinking
- Excessive perspiration
- Stinky feet
- Having an abnormally pale face
- Having a spaced-out, expressionless face
- Heart irregularities
- Snoring
- Fatigue
- Bad breath
- Excessive saliva
- Coated or patchy tongue (one that is partially coated and looks like a map)
- Weight gain or an inability to lose weight
- Joint pain or stiffness
- Restless legs
- Excessive or urgent need to urinate, or bedwetting
- Acute sensitivity to normal sounds
- Emotional or behavioral changes, such as anxiety, hyperactivity, irritability, or depression[10]

I personally experienced the weight gain and inability to lose weight, even though I tried many different diets. In my opinion, *it ain't just the diet* that made me hang onto the pounds. Since I kept giving my body foods that it could not use because it was allergic or sensitive to them, my body thought it was starving. And a starving body is going to hold onto every pound it can, right? When I eliminated the foods that caused me problems, I lost more than 40 pounds without actually dieting.

Adapting to Food Allergens

If you are truly allergic to a food, it's likely that you are aware of it because an allergic response happens almost immediately and is usually severe. On the other hand, if you are either sensitive to a food or intolerant of it, you may not realize the food is causing or contributing to your health issues.

You can also *adapt to foods* you are allergic to.

"Normal human adaptation responses make up one major built-in defense response to help protect our bodies," says Dr. Rapp. "…The second state is the addiction phase, or one of adaptation or masking. Cause-and-effect relationships are no longer obvious; they are masked. The person's body adjusts to some food or odor in such a way that illness is not noted."[11]

Like me, you may have developed an allergy to which your body has adapted over the years. I fed my body that food (soy milk) every day, and initially did not have a reaction. I started using soy milk on my cereal daily during my thirties because I read that soy can help with perimenopause symptoms, like hot flashes. It did not alleviate my symptoms, but I liked the taste of soy milk better than the low-fat milk I had been drinking for years, so I began to ingest it daily with no apparent ill effects. However, as time went on, I became allergic to it, and (probably because I ate it every day) my body adapted to it.

Simultaneously over time, I began to have serious allergic reactions every spring when the trees leafed out. At other times of the year, I had minor, unidentified symptoms of allergies.

It was only after I stopped using soy milk daily on my cereal, and then reintroduced it, that I discovered my severe soy allergy. Thankfully, I did not go into anaphylactic shock. But I did have a strong reaction that had me taking antihistamines and heading straight to bed for the day.

When I gave up soy milk, my spring-pollen allergies almost completely disappeared. Immediately. I believe my allergy to soy heightened my pollen allergies, causing the chaos.

Bowel Movements Can Be Enlightening

Before I started to track the foods I was eating and the subsequent symptoms I experienced, I must admit I didn't give bowel movements (BMs) much thought. If a doctor asked whether my BMs were normal, I always replied, "Yes."

Because who knows what normal is?

Guess what? There's a chart that health professionals use to classify bowel movements. And it's really quite helpful. It's called the Bristol Stool Form Scale. The chart was initially developed by Ken Heaton, M.D. and 66 volunteers at the University of Bristol, Bristol, U.K., while working on irritable bowel syndrome in 1997.[12]

It is now used internationally as a diagnostic and communication tool to help healthcare professionals evaluate diseases and treatments. It helps them understand how much time it takes food to travel through a person's system, until it leaves as waste, and can point them toward a medical solution.[13]

The chart can help you, too. I provide a copy of it on page 11.

First, when you note the details of your BM, you will be able to honestly answer your healthcare professional when they ask whether there has been any change in your BMs. In some health situations, this is critical information. Second, you won't have to wonder when the last time you passed your stool was. Third, knowing the frequency, timing, shape, and consistency of your BMs is an excellent way to discover how food is affecting you and your health.

But that means you not only have to write it down, you have to turn around and *look in the toilet* after you have a BM. (It's really not that disgusting. You can do it.)

The Bristol Stool Form Scale

Type 1		Separate hard lumps, like nuts (hard to pass)
Type 2		Sausage-shaped, but lumpy
Type 3		Like a sausage, but with cracks on its surface
Type 4		Like a sausage or snake, smooth and soft
Type 5		Soft blobs with clear-cut eges (passed easily)
Type 6		Fluffy pieces with ragged edges, a mushy stool
Type 7		Watery, no solid pieces, ENTIRELY LIQUID

Distributed with the kind permission of Dr K. W. Heaton; formerly reader in Medicine at the University of Bristol. Reproduced as a service to the medical profession by Norgine Ltd.
©2017 Norgine group of companies.
UKE-COR-NP-2000042. Date of preparation: May 2020
Converted with permission to black-and-white for this publication.[14]

According to WebMD:
"The ideal stool is generally type 3 or 4, easy to pass without being too watery. If yours is type 1 or 2, you're probably constipated. Types 5, 6, and 7 tend toward diarrhea."[15]

Track Your Symptoms & Get Help

To help you figure out what your food-related symptoms are, I have created a chart of symptoms (see next page) that people with food allergies, sensitivities, and intolerances often experience.

You may have some or all of the symptoms listed in this section. However, please note that many of these symptoms *can be caused by reasons other than food*, such as stress, heart disease, diabetes, thyroid issues, and others.

This means your reactions could be the *result of a disease that needs a doctor's care* and are not necessarily related to food allergies.

If you experience these symptoms, please fill out the checklist and take it with you to discuss your concerns with your doctor or other healthcare professional. Noting your symptoms will be invaluable in that discussion.

Put a check mark on the form next to any symptom you have noticed after eating (currently or in the recent past).

When you begin to track your food and symptoms in your *It Ain't Just the Diet Food Journal* daily log pages, pay special attention to any symptoms that you currently experience, noting them in your daily food tracker.

Then, each week on the *Symptoms Checklist*, check off the symptoms you experienced over the previous seven days. You may begin to see a pattern or to identify your particular food triggers.

You will find a blank Symptoms Checklist on the next page, as well as in the daily log section inserted every seven days for you to summarize what you are learning about yourself. I suggest you fill out the form right now to get a baseline of where you are today.

Food Allergies, Sensitivities, & Intolerances Symptoms Checklist

Initial Assessment

Date: _____

Check each symptom you have experienced after eating (currently or in the recent past).

Breathing
- ☐ Sneezing
- ☐ Stuffy nose/sinuses
- ☐ Congestion
- ☐ Runny nose
- ☐ Face pain
- ☐ Difficulty breathing
- ☐ Wheezing or asthma

Skin
- ☐ Hives
- ☐ Eczema or rash
- ☐ Dandruff
- ☐ Ticklishness
- ☐ Flushing
- ☐ Rosy cheeks or ears

Eyes
- ☐ Itchy eyes
- ☐ Dry eyes

Digestive
- ☐ Bloating
- ☐ Gas
- ☐ Constipated
- ☐ Diarrhea or loose stools
- ☐ More bowel movements
- ☐ Fewer bowel movements
- ☐ Abdominal cramping
- ☐ Stinky bowel movements
- ☐ Undigested food in stool
- ☐ Bloody stool

Brain/Thinking
- ☐ Brain fog
- ☐ Inability to concentrate
- ☐ Disjointed or distractible thinking
- ☐ Headaches
- ☐ Glassy-eyed or spacey
- ☐ Trouble remembering things

Energy
- ☐ Hyperactivity
- ☐ Restlessness
- ☐ Tiredness/fatigue
- ☐ Low energy/activity

Difference in Sleep
- ☐ Better
- ☐ Worse
- ☐ Restless leg while sleeping
- ☐ Ideas why? _____

Pain
- ☐ Joint pain
- ☐ Muscle pain
- ☐ Other pain: _____

Mood
- ☐ Ecstatic
- ☐ Happy
- ☐ Neutral
- ☐ Sad
- ☐ Angry/Irritable
- ☐ Calm
- ☐ Anxious
- ☐ Feeling stressed (hair on fire)
- ☐ Filled with creativity
- ☐ Exhausted/no energy

Hunger Changes
- ☐ Craving certain foods (list) _____
- ☐ Hungry all the time
- ☐ Little or no interest in food

Other
- ☐ Bad breath
- ☐ Stinky feet
- ☐ Sweating hands/feet
- ☐ Other: _____

Notes:
_____
_____
_____
_____
_____
_____
_____
_____
_____
_____

Testing for Food Allergies, Sensitivities & Intolerances
I suggest you become systematic in your approach to testing for food-related problems. Write everything down. I provide a handy *Food & Wellness Daily Log* form in the next chapter for you to use.

As a place to start to inform your testing, consider what you know about your reactions to the eight most common food allergies listed earlier:

- Egg
- Fish
- Milk
- Peanut
- Shellfish (crustaceans)
- Soy
- Tree nuts
- Wheat (gluten)

Remember that there can be a time-delay between when you eat something and when you have a reaction, so it's easy to think that one food is causing a problem when the culprit is something entirely different. In addition, the problem might be some kind of food pairing—like eating cheese and drinking a glass of wine. Or you can be allergic to raw apples but not cooked apples. So, it may take a long time to sort through it. And you may need professional help.

Single-elimination Diet Process
One way to do a "quick" test on a food is to do a single-elimination test, meaning you test only one food category at a time. That category includes *every form of the food within the category* you are testing. For instance, the category of dairy would include milk, cheese, sour cream, yogurt, casein, butter, cottage cheese, ricotta, etc.

To determine which category to test first, make a list of all your favorite foods. Why would you want to start with your favorite foods? I'm sorry to tell you, but they are the most likely offenders for your food-related problems.

Say what?

I know, it stinks that the foods you really love and crave are the ones that most likely cause problems for you. But it's true.[16]

Now determine the commonalities between the foods you listed as your favorites. For example, you might love bread, pastries, and pasta. What do these foods have in common? Wheat (gluten).

Test your overlapping favorite foods first. You are likely allergic or sensitive to them or something that is common in all of them.

In a single-elimination diet test, you should totally eliminate every form of the suspected food for *four days*, and then on the fifth day, *after not eating anything for at least four hours*, eat *only* the product you are testing.[17]

It is easiest to start this process at breakfast. You would eat no dairy, for instance, for four days. Then at breakfast, eat cottage cheese, a glass of milk, and a piece of cheese. That is, on the beginning of the fifth day, you sort of "load up" on the suspected allergen. Throughout the day, continue to eat only foods from the category you are testing. On your daily log page, note any physical, mental (including mood), or behavioral reactions throughout the day.

Be sure to continue your test with only one category at a time until you have a definite result. At the conclusion of testing day, you will probably know if a food causes you problems. If it is not clear to you, but you think you experienced a negative response, it might be time to get help with your testing.

To summarize, here's how you do a single-elimination diet test:

1. Pick one category of foods (for instance, dairy).
2. Read all labels and *do not eat any* foods within the chosen food category for four days (not one bite).
3. Beginning with breakfast on the fifth day, *after eating nothing for at least four hours*, eat *only* products containing your chosen food.
4. On this testing day, eat multiple types of the chosen food (in one sitting), for instance, a piece of cheese, a glass of milk and some cottage cheese.
5. Throughout the day, eat no foods other than the one category you are testing.
6. Write down any symptoms you experience and when they occur.

This can be a definitive test and you may know quickly if the food bothers you. When I tested dairy, I ate about two ounces of mozzarella cheese and was hit with severe joint pain within an hour. The pain lasted for nearly a week. *Voilà!* I had my answer.

However, if you do not have a clear reaction, you may still be allergic or sensitive to the food. You may have to do additional testing or get help. That's what happened to me when I tested gluten. My reactions to gluten are delayed; it takes about three days for it to bother me (and Dr. Rapp says it can take up to six days for some reactions to manifest). But by keeping a food journal, I eventually realized the connection to various symptoms.

When I finally gave up both dairy and gluten, I began to slowly heal my body, lose weight, and feel better.

I hope that reading my brief but troubled allergy history here will inspire you. I suggest you start tracking the foods (and potentially other lifestyle or environmental issues) that may be causing your health problems, and you discover how you can heal.

I know that if I can do it, you can too.

Notes:

CHAPTER 2
How to Use This Journal

2

> *"Let food be thy medicine and medicine be thy food."*
> ~ *Hippocrates (Greek Physician and Philosopher)*

Symptom Checkers & Daily Food Logs

On the following pages, you will find 13 weeks of daily food and wellness log forms (91 forms) to help you identify what foods (and possibly other issues) are causing problems for you.

Once a week I include a weekly symptom checklist so you can summarize your suspicions and previous week's findings. This should help you zero in on your food-related concerns.

I encourage you to fill out each daily form completely. Write down everything you eat and where and when you are eating it. This information is important because your problems might be related to rushing through meals, standing while eating, or any number of factors unrelated to food sensitivities. When you note the location, you may realize that your upset stomach is a result of stuffing that bagel in your mouth as you rush to work rather than an allergy to gluten. Or, you might see that you are eating more snacks because you are now working from home, sitting at the kitchen table near the snacks pantry. And this increase in food may be the true cause of your health issues.

Track Everything

Note how you feel physically, emotionally, and mentally. Track your sleep, water intake (which directly affects your BMs), and bowel movements. Exercise even though you don't feel like it. Trust me, it does get easier. You've only got one body; take care of it and it will last a *long* time.

If you take medications and/or vitamins, write down any new ones you begin so you can look back if problems start to creep up. If you suspect your medications are causing problems, note the side effects, and talk to your doctor immediately. Sometimes medications and vitamins contain gluten or other allergens, so be sure to read the labels and clarify the ingredients with your pharmacist to avoid accidentally ingesting the foods that make you sick.

If your healthcare professional has asked you to take your blood sugar levels or blood pressure readings daily or periodically, write them down on your log sheet. There is also a space to record your weight. I suggest you do this weekly. When you go to the doctor, take your logbook with you. It will be a treasure trove of information for your discussion with your doctor.

The *It Ain't Just the Diet Food Journal* daily food diary log form is designed for you to note if you are testing a particular food. Keep track of what food you are testing and any changes or reactions you see and feel. If you are sensitive, intolerant, or allergic to the food you are testing, you will most likely start to see a pattern.

Note that in this phase of discovery, you are not eliminating any foods. You are merely tracking what you are eating and any reactions you have. After you track your food for a little while, you may see a pattern developing and realize you should be doing a single-elimination diet test.

I show you how to fill out the forms on the next few pages. Now let's get started...

Food Allergies, Sensitivities, & Intolerances Symptoms Checklist

- Sample -

Initial Assessment   Date: _12 / 1 / 2020_

Check each symptom you have experienced after eating (currently or in the recent past).

Breathing
- ☐ Sneezing
- ☑ Stuffy nose/sinuses
- ☑ Congestion
- ☐ Runny nose
- ☐ Face pain
- ☑ Difficulty breathing
- ☐ Wheezing or asthma

Skin
- ☐ Hives
- ☐ Eczema or rash
- ☑ Dandruff
- ☐ Ticklishness
- ☑ Flushing
- ☐ Rosy cheeks or ears

Eyes
- ☑ Itchy eyes
- ☑ Dry eyes

Digestive
- ☑ Bloating
- ☑ Gas
- ☑ Constipated
- ☐ Diarrhea or loose stools
- ☐ More bowel movements
- ☑ Fewer bowel movements
- ☐ Abdominal cramping
- ☑ Stinky bowel movements
- ☐ Undigested food in stool
- ☐ Bloody stool

Brain/Thinking
- ☑ Brain fog
- ☑ Inability to concentrate
- ☑ Disjointed or distractible thinking
- ☐ Headaches
- ☐ Glassy-eyed or spacey
- ☑ Trouble remembering things

Energy
- ☐ Hyperactivity
- ☑ Restlessness
- ☑ Tiredness/fatigue
- ☐ Low energy/activity

Difference in Sleep
- ☐ Better
- ☑ Worse
- ☐ Restless leg while sleeping
- ☐ Ideas why? _____

Pain
- ☑ Joint pain
- ☐ Muscle pain
- ☐ Other pain: _____

Mood
- ☐ Ecstatic
- ☐ Happy
- ☑ Neutral
- ☐ Sad
- ☐ Angry/Irritable
- ☐ Calm
- ☑ Anxious
- ☑ Feeling stressed (hair on fire)
- ☐ Filled with creativity
- ☐ Exhausted/no energy

Hunger Changes
- ☑ Craving certain foods (list) _bread, ice cream_
- ☐ Hungry all the time
- ☐ Little or no interest in food

Other
- ☐ Bad breath
- ☑ Stinky feet
- ☑ Sweating hands/feet
- ☐ Other: _____

Notes:
_____
_____
_____
_____
_____
_____
_____
_____
_____
_____
_____
_____
_____

IT AIN'T JUST THE DIET
FOOD & WELLNESS DAILY LOG

Date: __12 / 1 / 2020__ Test Day # __1__

Circle your suspected problem foods.
Common allergens: citrus, coffee, corn, (dairy,)
eggs, fish/shellfish, gluten, meat (beef, lamb,
pork), peanuts, raw fruits & vegetables, soy,
tree nuts

WHAT DID YOU EAT TODAY?

Meal #1, Time/Location __7:30 A Kitchen__
Oatmeal, banana,
Walnuts, Milk
Coffee

Snack #1, Time/Location _____

Meal #2, Time/Location __12:30 P Kitchen__
Cream of Potato Soup
Salad w/ Ranch

Snack #2, Time/Location __3 P Desk__
Apple

Meal #3, Time/Location __6:30 P Kitchen__
Grilled Chicken
Broccoli
Roasted Sweet Potato

Snack #3, Time/Location __8 P Family Rm__
Cupcake

EXERCISE: What exercise did you do today?
How long? How do you feel?
Yoga, 30M
Walk 45M
Tired, Joints hurt

HOW DO YOU FEEL?
(Include Symptom/Time)

Achy today

8:30 A
Feeling bloated
Have back pain

Needed quick/urgent
Bathroom @ 2 P

Tired

Feeling better

Craving sweets

WATER: Cross off each 8-ounce glass of water
you drank today. (Mark other beverages with
meals.)

1 2 3 4 5 6 7 8 9 10

- Sample -

LAST NIGHT'S SLEEP

When did you fall asleep last night? __11 P__

When did you wake this morning? __6:30 A__

How well did you sleep last night? (Rate from 1-10, with 10 being best) __4__

Comments about sleep
__Restless; painful hip__

NEW MEDICATIONS/VITAMINS: List new medications. What side effects did you observe?
__None new__

VITALS

Blood Sugar/Time __95__ / __6:30 A__
Blood Sugar/Time __110__ / __9:30 P__

Blood Pressure/Time _____/_____
Blood Pressure/Time _____/_____

Weight __156.2__

BOWEL MOVEMENTS

BM No. 1/Time __9:30 A__
BM Type (Circle) 1 2 3 4 5 ⑥ 7

Observations: __Ugh. Don't feel well.__

BM No. 2/Time __2 P__
BM Type (Circle) 1 2 3 4 ⑤ 6 7

Observations: __Feel better now__
__but tired.__

BM No. 3/Time _____
BM Type (Circle) 1 2 3 4 5 6 7

Observations: _____

What challenge did you overcome today?
__Staying focused was hard.__

What are you grateful for?
__My family__

What's the best thing that happened today?
__I went for a walk in the sunshine__
__with my husband.__

Notes:

_____
_____
_____
_____
_____
_____
_____
_____
_____
_____
_____
_____
_____
_____
_____
_____
_____
_____
_____
_____
_____
_____
_____
_____
_____
_____
_____
_____
_____
_____
_____
_____
_____
_____
_____
_____
_____

CHAPTER 3
Symptom Trackers
& Daily Food Logs

3

"One cannot think well, love well, sleep well, if one has not dined well."
~ *Virginia Woolf (English Novelist)*

Food Allergies, Sensitivities, & Intolerances Symptoms Checklist

Week 1 Assessment

Date: _____

Check each symptom you have experienced after eating (currently or in the recent past).

Breathing
- ☐ Sneezing
- ☐ Stuffy nose/sinuses
- ☐ Congestion
- ☐ Runny nose
- ☐ Face pain
- ☐ Difficulty breathing
- ☐ Wheezing or asthma

Skin
- ☐ Hives
- ☐ Eczema or rash
- ☐ Dandruff
- ☐ Ticklishness
- ☐ Flushing
- ☐ Rosy cheeks or ears

Eyes
- ☐ Itchy eyes
- ☐ Dry eyes

Digestive
- ☐ Bloating
- ☐ Gas
- ☐ Constipated
- ☐ Diarrhea or loose stools
- ☐ More bowel movements
- ☐ Fewer bowel movements
- ☐ Abdominal cramping
- ☐ Stinky bowel movements
- ☐ Undigested food in stool
- ☐ Bloody stool

Brain/Thinking
- ☐ Brain fog
- ☐ Inability to concentrate
- ☐ Disjointed or distractible thinking
- ☐ Headaches
- ☐ Glassy-eyed or spacey
- ☐ Trouble remembering things

Energy
- ☐ Hyperactivity
- ☐ Restlessness
- ☐ Tiredness/fatigue
- ☐ Low energy/activity

Difference in Sleep
- ☐ Better
- ☐ Worse
- ☐ Restless leg while sleeping
- ☐ Ideas why? _____

Pain
- ☐ Joint pain
- ☐ Muscle pain
- ☐ Other pain: _____

Mood
- ☐ Ecstatic
- ☐ Happy
- ☐ Neutral
- ☐ Sad
- ☐ Angry/Irritable
- ☐ Calm
- ☐ Anxious
- ☐ Feeling stressed (hair on fire)
- ☐ Filled with creativity
- ☐ Exhausted/no energy

Hunger Changes
- ☐ Craving certain foods (list) _____
- ☐ Hungry all the time
- ☐ Little or no interest in food

Other
- ☐ Bad breath
- ☐ Stinky feet
- ☐ Sweating hands/feet
- ☐ Other: _____

Notes:
_____
_____
_____
_____
_____
_____
_____
_____
_____
_____

Week 1 Journal Prompt

Write about your favorite food memory. Who does it involve?
When and where did it occur? How old were you? Why is it your favorite?

_____
_____
_____
_____
_____
_____
_____
_____
_____
_____
_____
_____
_____
_____
_____
_____
_____
_____
_____
_____
_____
_____
_____
_____
_____
_____
_____
_____
_____
_____
_____

IT AIN'T JUST THE DIET
FOOD & WELLNESS DAILY LOG

Date: _____   Test Day #_____

Circle your suspected problem foods.
Common allergens: citrus, coffee, corn, dairy,
eggs, fish/shellfish, gluten, meat (beef, lamb,
pork), peanuts, raw fruits & vegetables, soy,
tree nuts

WHAT DID YOU EAT TODAY?

Meal #1, Time/Location _____
_____
_____
_____

Snack #1, Time/Location _____
_____
_____

Meal #2, Time/Location _____
_____
_____
_____

Snack #2, Time/Location _____
_____
_____

Meal #3, Time/Location _____
_____
_____
_____

Snack #3, Time/Location _____
_____
_____

HOW DO YOU FEEL?
(Include Symptom/Time)
_____
_____
_____
_____
_____
_____
_____
_____
_____
_____
_____
_____
_____
_____
_____
_____
_____
_____
_____
_____
_____
_____
_____
_____
_____
_____
_____
_____
_____
_____
_____
_____
_____
_____
_____

EXERCISE: What exercise did you do today?
How long? How do you feel?
_____
_____
_____

WATER: Cross off each 8-ounce glass of water
you drank today. (Mark other beverages with
meals.)

1   2   3   4   5   6   7   8   9   10

Week 1 Journal Prompt

Write about your favorite food memory. Who does it involve?
When and where did it occur? How old were you? Why is it your favorite?

_____
_____
_____
_____
_____
_____
_____
_____
_____
_____
_____
_____
_____
_____
_____
_____
_____
_____
_____
_____
_____
_____
_____
_____
_____
_____
_____
_____
_____
_____

IT AIN'T JUST THE DIET
FOOD & WELLNESS DAILY LOG

Date: _____ Test Day #_____

Circle your suspected problem foods.
Common allergens: citrus, coffee, corn, dairy,
eggs, fish/shellfish, gluten, meat (beef, lamb,
pork), peanuts, raw fruits & vegetables, soy,
tree nuts

WHAT DID YOU EAT TODAY?

Meal #1, Time/Location _____
_____
_____
_____

Snack #1, Time/Location _____
_____
_____

Meal #2, Time/Location _____
_____
_____
_____

Snack #2, Time/Location _____
_____
_____

Meal #3, Time/Location _____
_____
_____
_____

Snack #3, Time/Location _____
_____
_____

HOW DO YOU FEEL?
(Include Symptom/Time)
_____
_____
_____
_____
_____
_____
_____
_____
_____
_____
_____
_____
_____
_____
_____
_____
_____
_____
_____
_____
_____
_____
_____
_____
_____
_____
_____
_____
_____
_____
_____
_____

EXERCISE: What exercise did you do today?
How long? How do you feel?
_____
_____
_____

WATER: Cross off each 8-ounce glass of water
you drank today. (Mark other beverages with
meals.)

1   2   3   4   5   6   7   8   9   10

LAST NIGHT'S SLEEP

When did you fall asleep last night? _____

When did you wake this morning? _____

How well did you sleep last night? (Rate from 1-10, with 10 being best) _____

Comments about sleep

_____
_____
_____
_____
_____
_____
_____
_____
_____
_____
_____
_____
_____
_____

NEW MEDICATIONS/VITAMINS: List new medications. What side effects did you observe?

_____
_____
_____
_____
_____
_____
_____
_____
_____
_____
_____
_____
_____
_____

VITALS

Blood Sugar/Time _____/_____
Blood Sugar/Time _____/_____

Blood Pressure/Time _____/_____
Blood Pressure/Time _____/_____

Weight _____

BOWEL MOVEMENTS

BM No. 1/Time_____
BM Type (Circle) 1 2 3 4 5 6 7

Observations: _____
_____
_____

BM No. 2/Time_____
BM Type (Circle) 1 2 3 4 5 6 7

Observations: _____
_____
_____

BM No. 3/Time_____
BM Type (Circle) 1 2 3 4 5 6 7

Observations: _____
_____
_____

What challenge did you overcome today?
_____
_____
_____

What are you grateful for?
_____
_____
_____

What's the best thing that happened today?
_____
_____
_____

IT AIN'T JUST THE DIET
FOOD & WELLNESS DAILY LOG

Date: _____ Test Day #_____

Circle your suspected problem foods.
Common allergens: citrus, coffee, corn, dairy,
eggs, fish/shellfish, gluten, meat (beef, lamb,
pork), peanuts, raw fruits & vegetables, soy,
tree nuts

WHAT DID YOU EAT TODAY?

Meal #1, Time/Location _____
_____
_____
_____
_____

Snack #1, Time/Location _____
_____
_____

Meal #2, Time/Location _____
_____
_____
_____
_____

Snack #2, Time/Location _____
_____
_____

Meal #3, Time/Location _____
_____
_____
_____
_____

Snack #3, Time/Location _____
_____
_____

EXERCISE: What exercise did you do today?
How long? How do you feel?
_____
_____
_____

HOW DO YOU FEEL?
(Include Symptom/Time)

_____
_____
_____
_____
_____
_____
_____
_____
_____
_____
_____
_____
_____
_____
_____
_____
_____
_____
_____
_____
_____
_____
_____
_____
_____
_____
_____
_____
_____
_____
_____
_____
_____
_____
_____

WATER: Cross off each 8-ounce glass of water
you drank today. (Mark other beverages with
meals.)

1   2   3   4   5   6   7   8   9   10

LAST NIGHT'S SLEEP

When did you fall asleep last night? _____

When did you wake this morning? _____

How well did you sleep last night? (Rate from 1-10, with 10 being best) _____

Comments about sleep

_____

_____

_____

_____

_____

_____

_____

_____

_____

_____

_____

_____

_____

_____

_____

NEW MEDICATIONS/VITAMINS: List new medications. What side effects did you observe?

_____

_____

_____

_____

_____

_____

_____

_____

_____

_____

_____

_____

VITALS

Blood Sugar/Time _____ / _____

Blood Sugar/Time _____ / _____

Blood Pressure/Time _____ / _____

Blood Pressure/Time _____ / _____

Weight _____

BOWEL MOVEMENTS

BM No. 1/Time_____

BM Type (Circle) 1   2   3   4   5   6   7

Observations: _____

_____

_____

BM No. 2/Time_____

BM Type (Circle) 1   2   3   4   5   6   7

Observations: _____

_____

_____

BM No. 3/Time_____

BM Type (Circle) 1   2   3   4   5   6   7

Observations: _____

_____

_____

What challenge did you overcome today?

_____

_____

_____

What are you grateful for?

_____

_____

_____

What's the best thing that happened today?

_____

_____

_____

IT AIN'T JUST THE DIET
FOOD & WELLNESS DAILY LOG

Date: _____ Test Day #_____

Circle your suspected problem foods.
Common allergens: citrus, coffee, corn, dairy,
eggs, fish/shellfish, gluten, meat (beef, lamb,
pork), peanuts, raw fruits & vegetables, soy,
tree nuts

WHAT DID YOU EAT TODAY?

Meal #1, Time/Location _____
_____
_____
_____

Snack #1, Time/Location _____
_____
_____

Meal #2, Time/Location _____
_____
_____
_____

Snack #2, Time/Location _____
_____
_____

Meal #3, Time/Location _____
_____
_____
_____

Snack #3, Time/Location _____
_____
_____

HOW DO YOU FEEL?
(Include Symptom/Time)
_____
_____
_____
_____
_____
_____
_____
_____
_____
_____
_____
_____
_____
_____
_____
_____
_____
_____
_____
_____
_____
_____
_____
_____
_____
_____
_____
_____
_____
_____
_____
_____
_____

EXERCISE: What exercise did you do today?
How long? How do you feel?
_____
_____
_____

WATER: Cross off each 8-ounce glass of water
you drank today. (Mark other beverages with
meals.)

1   2   3   4   5   6   7   8   9   10

LAST NIGHT'S SLEEP

When did you fall asleep last night? _____

When did you wake this morning? _____

How well did you sleep last night? (Rate from 1-10, with 10 being best) _____

Comments about sleep

_____
_____
_____
_____
_____
_____
_____
_____
_____
_____
_____
_____
_____
_____
_____
_____
_____
_____
_____

NEW MEDICATIONS/VITAMINS: List new medications. What side effects did you observe?

_____
_____
_____
_____
_____
_____
_____
_____
_____
_____
_____
_____
_____
_____
_____
_____

VITALS

Blood Sugar/Time _____/_____

Blood Sugar/Time _____/_____

Blood Pressure/Time _____/_____

Blood Pressure/Time _____/_____

Weight _____

BOWEL MOVEMENTS

BM No. 1/Time_____

BM Type (Circle) 1   2   3   4   5   6   7

Observations: _____
_____
_____

BM No. 2/Time_____

BM Type (Circle) 1   2   3   4   5   6   7

Observations: _____
_____
_____

BM No. 3/Time_____

BM Type (Circle) 1   2   3   4   5   6   7

Observations: _____
_____
_____

What challenge did you overcome today?

_____
_____
_____

What are you grateful for?

_____
_____
_____

What's the best thing that happened today?

_____
_____
_____

IT AIN'T JUST THE DIET
FOOD & WELLNESS DAILY LOG

Date: _____ Test Day # _____

Circle your suspected problem foods.
Common allergens: citrus, coffee, corn, dairy, eggs, fish/shellfish, gluten, meat (beef, lamb, pork), peanuts, raw fruits & vegetables, soy, tree nuts

WHAT DID YOU EAT TODAY?

Meal #1, Time/Location _____
_____
_____
_____

Snack #1, Time/Location _____
_____
_____

Meal #2, Time/Location _____
_____
_____
_____

Snack #2, Time/Location _____
_____
_____

Meal #3, Time/Location _____
_____
_____
_____

Snack #3, Time/Location _____
_____
_____

EXERCISE: What exercise did you do today? How long? How do you feel?
_____
_____
_____

HOW DO YOU FEEL?
(Include Symptom/Time)
_____
_____
_____
_____
_____
_____
_____
_____
_____
_____
_____
_____
_____
_____
_____
_____
_____
_____
_____
_____
_____
_____
_____
_____
_____
_____
_____
_____
_____
_____
_____
_____
_____
_____
_____
_____

WATER: Cross off each 8-ounce glass of water you drank today. (Mark other beverages with meals.)

1   2   3   4   5   6   7   8   9   10

LAST NIGHT'S SLEEP

When did you fall asleep last night? _____

When did you wake this morning? _____

How well did you sleep last night? (Rate from 1-10, with 10 being best) _____

Comments about sleep

_____
_____
_____
_____
_____
_____
_____
_____
_____
_____
_____
_____
_____
_____
_____
_____
_____
_____

NEW MEDICATIONS/VITAMINS: List new medications. What side effects did you observe?

_____
_____
_____
_____
_____
_____
_____
_____
_____
_____
_____
_____
_____
_____
_____

VITALS

Blood Sugar/Time _____/_____
Blood Sugar/Time _____/_____

Blood Pressure/Time _____/_____
Blood Pressure/Time _____/_____

Weight _____

BOWEL MOVEMENTS

BM No. 1/Time_____
BM Type (Circle) 1   2   3   4   5   6   7

Observations: _____
_____
_____

BM No. 2/Time_____
BM Type (Circle) 1   2   3   4   5   6   7

Observations: _____
_____
_____

BM No. 3/Time_____
BM Type (Circle) 1   2   3   4   5   6   7

Observations: _____
_____
_____

What challenge did you overcome today?
_____
_____
_____

What are you grateful for?
_____
_____
_____

What's the best thing that happened today?
_____
_____
_____

IT AIN'T JUST THE DIET
FOOD & WELLNESS DAILY LOG

Date: _____ Test Day #_____

Circle your suspected problem foods.
Common allergens: citrus, coffee, corn, dairy, eggs, fish/shellfish, gluten, meat (beef, lamb, pork), peanuts, raw fruits & vegetables, soy, tree nuts

WHAT DID YOU EAT TODAY?

Meal #1, Time/Location _____
_____
_____
_____

Snack #1, Time/Location _____
_____
_____

Meal #2, Time/Location _____
_____
_____
_____

Snack #2, Time/Location _____
_____
_____

Meal #3, Time/Location _____
_____
_____
_____

Snack #3, Time/Location _____
_____
_____

HOW DO YOU FEEL?
(Include Symptom/Time)
_____
_____
_____
_____
_____
_____
_____
_____
_____
_____
_____
_____
_____
_____
_____
_____
_____
_____
_____
_____
_____
_____
_____
_____
_____
_____
_____
_____
_____
_____
_____
_____

EXERCISE: What exercise did you do today? How long? How do you feel?
_____
_____
_____

WATER: Cross off each 8-ounce glass of water you drank today. (Mark other beverages with meals.)

1   2   3   4   5   6   7   8   9   10

LAST NIGHT'S SLEEP

When did you fall asleep last night? _____

When did you wake this morning? _____

How well did you sleep last night? (Rate from 1-10, with 10 being best) _____

Comments about sleep

_____
_____
_____
_____
_____
_____
_____
_____
_____
_____
_____
_____
_____
_____
_____
_____
_____
_____

NEW MEDICATIONS/VITAMINS: List new medications. What side effects did you observe?

_____
_____
_____
_____
_____
_____
_____
_____
_____
_____
_____
_____
_____
_____
_____
_____

VITALS

Blood Sugar/Time _____ / _____
Blood Sugar/Time _____ / _____

Blood Pressure/Time _____ / _____
Blood Pressure/Time _____ / _____

Weight _____

BOWEL MOVEMENTS

BM No. 1/Time_____
BM Type (Circle) 1   2   3   4   5   6   7

Observations: _____
_____
_____

BM No. 2/Time_____
BM Type (Circle) 1   2   3   4   5   6   7

Observations: _____
_____
_____

BM No. 3/Time_____
BM Type (Circle) 1   2   3   4   5   6   7

Observations: _____
_____
_____

What challenge did you overcome today?

_____
_____
_____

What are you grateful for?

_____
_____
_____

What's the best thing that happened today?

_____
_____
_____

IT AIN'T JUST THE DIET
FOOD & WELLNESS DAILY LOG

Date: _____ Test Day #_____

Circle your suspected problem foods.
Common allergens: citrus, coffee, corn, dairy, eggs, fish/shellfish, gluten, meat (beef, lamb, pork), peanuts, raw fruits & vegetables, soy, tree nuts

WHAT DID YOU EAT TODAY?

Meal #1, Time/Location _____
_____
_____
_____

Snack #1, Time/Location _____
_____
_____

Meal #2, Time/Location _____
_____
_____
_____

Snack #2, Time/Location _____
_____
_____

Meal #3, Time/Location _____
_____
_____
_____

Snack #3, Time/Location _____
_____
_____

EXERCISE: What exercise did you do today? How long? How do you feel?
_____
_____
_____

HOW DO YOU FEEL?
(Include Symptom/Time)
_____
_____
_____
_____
_____
_____
_____
_____
_____
_____
_____
_____
_____
_____
_____
_____
_____
_____
_____
_____
_____
_____
_____
_____
_____
_____
_____
_____
_____
_____

WATER: Cross off each 8-ounce glass of water you drank today. (Mark other beverages with meals.)

1   2   3   4   5   6   7   8   9   10

LAST NIGHT'S SLEEP

When did you fall asleep last night? _____

When did you wake this morning? _____

How well did you sleep last night? (Rate from 1-10, with 10 being best) _____

Comments about sleep

_____
_____
_____
_____
_____
_____
_____
_____
_____
_____
_____
_____
_____
_____
_____
_____
_____
_____
_____
_____

NEW MEDICATIONS/VITAMINS: List new medications. What side effects did you observe?

_____
_____
_____
_____
_____
_____
_____
_____
_____
_____
_____
_____
_____
_____
_____
_____

VITALS

Blood Sugar/Time _____/_____
Blood Sugar/Time _____/_____

Blood Pressure/Time _____/_____
Blood Pressure/Time _____/_____

Weight _____

BOWEL MOVEMENTS

BM No. 1/Time_____
BM Type (Circle) 1   2   3   4   5   6   7

Observations: _____
_____
_____

BM No. 2/Time_____
BM Type (Circle) 1   2   3   4   5   6   7

Observations: _____
_____
_____

BM No. 3/Time_____
BM Type (Circle) 1   2   3   4   5   6   7

Observations: _____
_____
_____

What challenge did you overcome today?

_____
_____
_____

What are you grateful for?

_____
_____
_____

What's the best thing that happened today?

_____
_____
_____

IT AIN'T JUST THE DIET
FOOD & WELLNESS DAILY LOG

Date: _____ Test Day #_____

Circle your suspected problem foods.
Common allergens: citrus, coffee, corn, dairy, eggs, fish/shellfish, gluten, meat (beef, lamb, pork), peanuts, raw fruits & vegetables, soy, tree nuts

WHAT DID YOU EAT TODAY?

Meal #1, Time/Location _____
_____
_____
_____

Snack #1, Time/Location _____
_____
_____

Meal #2, Time/Location _____
_____
_____
_____

Snack #2, Time/Location _____
_____
_____

Meal #3, Time/Location _____
_____
_____
_____

Snack #3, Time/Location _____
_____
_____

HOW DO YOU FEEL?
(Include Symptom/Time)
_____
_____
_____
_____
_____
_____
_____
_____
_____
_____
_____
_____
_____
_____
_____
_____
_____
_____
_____
_____
_____
_____
_____
_____
_____
_____
_____
_____
_____
_____
_____
_____
_____
_____
_____
_____

EXERCISE: What exercise did you do today? How long? How do you feel?
_____
_____
_____

WATER: Cross off each 8-ounce glass of water you drank today. (Mark other beverages with meals.)

1   2   3   4   5   6   7   8   9   10

LAST NIGHT'S SLEEP

When did you fall asleep last night? _____

When did you wake this morning? _____

How well did you sleep last night? (Rate from 1-10, with 10 being best) _____

Comments about sleep

_____
_____
_____
_____
_____
_____
_____
_____
_____
_____
_____
_____
_____
_____
_____
_____
_____

NEW MEDICATIONS/VITAMINS: List new medications. What side effects did you observe?

_____
_____
_____
_____
_____
_____
_____
_____
_____
_____
_____
_____
_____
_____
_____

VITALS

Blood Sugar/Time _____/_____
Blood Sugar/Time _____/_____

Blood Pressure/Time _____/_____
Blood Pressure/Time _____/_____

Weight _____

BOWEL MOVEMENTS

BM No. 1/Time_____
BM Type (Circle) 1   2   3   4   5   6   7

Observations: _____
_____
_____

BM No. 2/Time_____
BM Type (Circle) 1   2   3   4   5   6   7

Observations: _____
_____
_____

BM No. 3/Time_____
BM Type (Circle) 1   2   3   4   5   6   7

Observations: _____
_____
_____

What challenge did you overcome today?
_____
_____
_____

What are you grateful for?
_____
_____
_____

What's the best thing that happened today?
_____
_____
_____

Food Allergies, Sensitivities, & Intolerances Symptoms Checklist

Week 2 Assessment

Date: _____

Check each symptom you have experienced after eating (currently or in the recent past).

Breathing
- ☐ Sneezing
- ☐ Stuffy nose/sinuses
- ☐ Congestion
- ☐ Runny nose
- ☐ Face pain
- ☐ Difficulty breathing
- ☐ Wheezing or asthma

Skin
- ☐ Hives
- ☐ Eczema or rash
- ☐ Dandruff
- ☐ Ticklishness
- ☐ Flushing
- ☐ Rosy cheeks or ears

Eyes
- ☐ Itchy eyes
- ☐ Dry eyes

Digestive
- ☐ Bloating
- ☐ Gas
- ☐ Constipated
- ☐ Diarrhea or loose stools
- ☐ More bowel movements
- ☐ Fewer bowel movements
- ☐ Abdominal cramping
- ☐ Stinky bowel movements
- ☐ Undigested food in stool
- ☐ Bloody stool

Brain/Thinking
- ☐ Brain fog
- ☐ Inability to concentrate
- ☐ Disjointed or distractible thinking
- ☐ Headaches
- ☐ Glassy-eyed or spacey
- ☐ Trouble remembering things

Energy
- ☐ Hyperactivity
- ☐ Restlessness
- ☐ Tiredness/fatigue
- ☐ Low energy/activity

Difference in Sleep
- ☐ Better
- ☐ Worse
- ☐ Restless leg while sleeping
- ☐ Ideas why? _____

Pain
- ☐ Joint pain
- ☐ Muscle pain
- ☐ Other pain: _____

Mood
- ☐ Ecstatic
- ☐ Happy
- ☐ Neutral
- ☐ Sad
- ☐ Angry/Irritable
- ☐ Calm
- ☐ Anxious
- ☐ Feeling stressed (hair on fire)
- ☐ Filled with creativity
- ☐ Exhausted/no energy

Hunger Changes
- ☐ Craving certain foods (list) _____
- ☐ Hungry all the time
- ☐ Little or no interest in food

Other
- ☐ Bad breath
- ☐ Stinky feet
- ☐ Sweating hands/feet
- ☐ Other: _____

Notes:
_____
_____
_____
_____
_____
_____
_____
_____
_____
_____
_____

Week 2 Journal Prompt

What is your favorite cookbook to use? And why?

_____
_____
_____
_____
_____
_____
_____
_____
_____
_____
_____
_____
_____
_____
_____
_____
_____
_____
_____
_____
_____
_____
_____
_____
_____
_____
_____
_____
_____
_____
_____
_____

IT AIN'T JUST THE DIET
FOOD & WELLNESS DAILY LOG

Date: _____ Test Day #_____

Circle your suspected problem foods.
Common allergens: citrus, coffee, corn, dairy, eggs, fish/shellfish, gluten, meat (beef, lamb, pork), peanuts, raw fruits & vegetables, soy, tree nuts

WHAT DID YOU EAT TODAY?

Meal #1, Time/Location _____
_____
_____
_____

Snack #1, Time/Location _____
_____
_____

Meal #2, Time/Location _____
_____
_____
_____

Snack #2, Time/Location _____
_____
_____

Meal #3, Time/Location _____
_____
_____
_____

Snack #3, Time/Location _____
_____
_____

HOW DO YOU FEEL?
(Include Symptom/Time)
_____
_____
_____
_____
_____
_____
_____
_____
_____
_____
_____
_____
_____
_____
_____
_____
_____
_____
_____
_____
_____
_____
_____
_____
_____
_____
_____
_____
_____
_____
_____
_____
_____

EXERCISE: What exercise did you do today? How long? How do you feel?
_____
_____
_____

WATER: Cross off each 8-ounce glass of water you drank today. (Mark other beverages with meals.)

1   2   3   4   5   6   7   8   9   10

LAST NIGHT'S SLEEP

When did you fall asleep last night? _____

When did you wake this morning? _____

How well did you sleep last night? (Rate from 1-10, with 10 being best) _____

Comments about sleep

_____
_____
_____
_____
_____
_____
_____
_____
_____
_____
_____
_____
_____
_____
_____
_____
_____
_____
_____

NEW MEDICATIONS/VITAMINS: List new medications. What side effects did you observe?

_____
_____
_____
_____
_____
_____
_____
_____
_____
_____
_____
_____
_____
_____
_____

VITALS

Blood Sugar/Time _____/_____
Blood Sugar/Time _____/_____

Blood Pressure/Time _____/_____
Blood Pressure/Time _____/_____

Weight _____

BOWEL MOVEMENTS

BM No. 1/Time_____
BM Type (Circle) 1   2   3   4   5   6   7

Observations: _____
_____
_____

BM No. 2/Time_____
BM Type (Circle) 1   2   3   4   5   6   7

Observations: _____
_____
_____

BM No. 3/Time_____
BM Type (Circle) 1   2   3   4   5   6   7

Observations: _____
_____
_____

What challenge did you overcome today?
_____
_____
_____

What are you grateful for?
_____
_____
_____

What's the best thing that happened today?
_____
_____
_____

IT AIN'T JUST THE DIET
FOOD & WELLNESS DAILY LOG

Date: _____ Test Day # _____

Circle your suspected problem foods.
Common allergens: citrus, coffee, corn, dairy, eggs, fish/shellfish, gluten, meat (beef, lamb, pork), peanuts, raw fruits & vegetables, soy, tree nuts

WHAT DID YOU EAT TODAY?

Meal #1, Time/Location _____
_____
_____
_____

Snack #1, Time/Location _____
_____
_____

Meal #2, Time/Location _____
_____
_____
_____

Snack #2, Time/Location _____
_____
_____

Meal #3, Time/Location _____
_____
_____
_____

Snack #3, Time/Location _____
_____
_____

HOW DO YOU FEEL?
(Include Symptom/Time)
_____
_____
_____
_____
_____
_____
_____
_____
_____
_____
_____
_____
_____
_____
_____
_____
_____
_____
_____
_____
_____
_____
_____
_____
_____
_____
_____
_____
_____
_____
_____
_____
_____
_____
_____

EXERCISE: What exercise did you do today? How long? How do you feel?
_____
_____
_____

WATER: Cross off each 8-ounce glass of water you drank today. (Mark other beverages with meals.)

1   2   3   4   5   6   7   8   9   10

LAST NIGHT'S SLEEP

When did you fall asleep last night? _____

When did you wake this morning? _____

How well did you sleep last night? (Rate from 1-10, with 10 being best) _____

Comments about sleep

_____
_____
_____
_____
_____
_____
_____
_____
_____
_____
_____
_____
_____
_____
_____
_____
_____

NEW MEDICATIONS/VITAMINS: List new medications. What side effects did you observe?

_____
_____
_____
_____
_____
_____
_____
_____
_____
_____
_____
_____
_____
_____
_____

VITALS

Blood Sugar/Time _____/_____
Blood Sugar/Time _____/_____

Blood Pressure/Time _____/_____
Blood Pressure/Time _____/_____

Weight _____

BOWEL MOVEMENTS

BM No. 1/Time_____
BM Type (Circle) 1   2   3   4   5   6   7

Observations: _____
_____
_____

BM No. 2/Time_____
BM Type (Circle) 1   2   3   4   5   6   7

Observations: _____
_____
_____

BM No. 3/Time_____
BM Type (Circle) 1   2   3   4   5   6   7

Observations: _____
_____
_____

What challenge did you overcome today?

_____
_____
_____

What are you grateful for?

_____
_____
_____

What's the best thing that happened today?

_____
_____
_____

IT AIN'T JUST THE DIET
FOOD & WELLNESS DAILY LOG

Date: _____ Test Day #_____

Circle your suspected problem foods.
Common allergens: citrus, coffee, corn, dairy, eggs, fish/shellfish, gluten, meat (beef, lamb, pork), peanuts, raw fruits & vegetables, soy, tree nuts

WHAT DID YOU EAT TODAY?

Meal #1, Time/Location _____
_____
_____
_____

Snack #1, Time/Location _____
_____
_____

Meal #2, Time/Location _____
_____
_____
_____

Snack #2, Time/Location _____
_____
_____

Meal #3, Time/Location _____
_____
_____
_____

Snack #3, Time/Location _____
_____
_____

HOW DO YOU FEEL?
(Include Symptom/Time)
_____
_____
_____
_____
_____
_____
_____
_____
_____
_____
_____
_____
_____
_____
_____
_____
_____
_____
_____
_____
_____
_____
_____
_____
_____
_____
_____
_____
_____
_____
_____
_____
_____

EXERCISE: What exercise did you do today? How long? How do you feel?
_____
_____
_____

WATER: Cross off each 8-ounce glass of water you drank today. (Mark other beverages with meals.)

1   2   3   4   5   6   7   8   9   10

LAST NIGHT'S SLEEP

When did you fall asleep last night? _____

When did you wake this morning? _____

How well did you sleep last night? (Rate from 1-10, with 10 being best) _____

Comments about sleep

_____
_____
_____
_____
_____
_____
_____
_____
_____
_____
_____
_____
_____
_____
_____
_____
_____
_____
_____
_____
_____

NEW MEDICATIONS/VITAMINS: List new medications. What side effects did you observe?

_____
_____
_____
_____
_____
_____
_____
_____
_____
_____
_____
_____
_____
_____
_____

VITALS

Blood Sugar/Time _____/_____
Blood Sugar/Time _____/_____

Blood Pressure/Time _____/_____
Blood Pressure/Time _____/_____

Weight _____

BOWEL MOVEMENTS

BM No. 1/Time_____
BM Type (Circle) 1   2   3   4   5   6   7

Observations: _____
_____
_____

BM No. 2/Time_____
BM Type (Circle) 1   2   3   4   5   6   7

Observations: _____
_____
_____

BM No. 3/Time_____
BM Type (Circle) 1   2   3   4   5   6   7

Observations: _____
_____
_____

What challenge did you overcome today?

_____
_____
_____

What are you grateful for?

_____
_____
_____

What's the best thing that happened today?

_____
_____
_____

IT AIN'T JUST THE DIET
FOOD & WELLNESS DAILY LOG

Date: _____ Test Day #_____

Circle your suspected problem foods.
Common allergens: citrus, coffee, corn, dairy,
eggs, fish/shellfish, gluten, meat (beef, lamb,
pork), peanuts, raw fruits & vegetables, soy,
tree nuts

WHAT DID YOU EAT TODAY?

Meal #1, Time/Location _____
_____
_____
_____

Snack #1, Time/Location _____
_____
_____

Meal #2, Time/Location _____
_____
_____
_____

Snack #2, Time/Location _____
_____
_____

Meal #3, Time/Location _____
_____
_____
_____

Snack #3, Time/Location _____
_____
_____

HOW DO YOU FEEL?
(Include Symptom/Time)
_____
_____
_____
_____
_____
_____
_____
_____
_____
_____
_____
_____
_____
_____
_____
_____
_____
_____
_____
_____
_____
_____
_____
_____
_____
_____
_____
_____
_____
_____
_____
_____
_____

EXERCISE: What exercise did you do today?
How long? How do you feel?
_____
_____
_____

WATER: Cross off each 8-ounce glass of water
you drank today. (Mark other beverages with
meals.)

1   2   3   4   5   6   7   8   9   10

LAST NIGHT'S SLEEP

When did you fall asleep last night? _____

When did you wake this morning? _____

How well did you sleep last night? (Rate from 1-10, with 10 being best) _____

Comments about sleep

_____
_____
_____
_____
_____
_____
_____
_____
_____
_____
_____
_____
_____
_____
_____
_____
_____
_____
_____
_____

NEW MEDICATIONS/VITAMINS: List new medications. What side effects did you observe?

_____
_____
_____
_____
_____
_____
_____
_____
_____
_____
_____
_____
_____
_____
_____
_____
_____

VITALS

Blood Sugar/Time _____ / _____
Blood Sugar/Time _____ / _____

Blood Pressure/Time _____ / _____
Blood Pressure/Time _____ / _____

Weight _____

BOWEL MOVEMENTS

BM No. 1/Time_____
BM Type (Circle) 1 2 3 4 5 6 7

Observations: _____
_____
_____

BM No. 2/Time_____
BM Type (Circle) 1 2 3 4 5 6 7

Observations: _____
_____
_____

BM No. 3/Time_____
BM Type (Circle) 1 2 3 4 5 6 7

Observations: _____
_____
_____

What challenge did you overcome today?

_____
_____
_____

What are you grateful for?

_____
_____
_____

What's the best thing that happened today?

_____
_____
_____

IT AIN'T JUST THE DIET
FOOD & WELLNESS DAILY LOG

Date: _____ Test Day #_____

Circle your suspected problem foods.
Common allergens: citrus, coffee, corn, dairy, eggs, fish/shellfish, gluten, meat (beef, lamb, pork), peanuts, raw fruits & vegetables, soy, tree nuts

WHAT DID YOU EAT TODAY?

Meal #1, Time/Location _____
_____
_____
_____

Snack #1, Time/Location _____
_____
_____

Meal #2, Time/Location _____
_____
_____
_____

Snack #2, Time/Location _____
_____
_____

Meal #3, Time/Location _____
_____
_____
_____

Snack #3, Time/Location _____
_____
_____

HOW DO YOU FEEL?
(Include Symptom/Time)

_____
_____
_____
_____
_____
_____
_____
_____
_____
_____
_____
_____
_____
_____
_____
_____
_____
_____
_____
_____
_____
_____
_____
_____
_____
_____
_____
_____
_____
_____
_____
_____

EXERCISE: What exercise did you do today? How long? How do you feel?
_____
_____
_____

WATER: Cross off each 8-ounce glass of water you drank today. (Mark other beverages with meals.)

1   2   3   4   5   6   7   8   9   10

LAST NIGHT'S SLEEP

When did you fall asleep last night? _____

When did you wake this morning? _____

How well did you sleep last night? (Rate from 1-10, with 10 being best) _____

Comments about sleep

_____
_____
_____
_____
_____
_____
_____
_____
_____
_____
_____
_____
_____
_____
_____
_____
_____
_____

NEW MEDICATIONS/VITAMINS: List new medications. What side effects did you observe?

_____
_____
_____
_____
_____
_____
_____
_____
_____
_____
_____
_____
_____

VITALS

Blood Sugar/Time _____/_____
Blood Sugar/Time _____/_____

Blood Pressure/Time _____/_____
Blood Pressure/Time _____/_____

Weight _____

BOWEL MOVEMENTS

BM No. 1/Time_____
BM Type (Circle) 1   2   3   4   5   6   7

Observations: _____
_____
_____

BM No. 2/Time_____
BM Type (Circle) 1   2   3   4   5   6   7

Observations: _____
_____
_____

BM No. 3/Time_____
BM Type (Circle) 1   2   3   4   5   6   7

Observations: _____
_____
_____

What challenge did you overcome today?
_____
_____
_____

What are you grateful for?
_____
_____
_____

What's the best thing that happened today?
_____
_____
_____

IT AIN'T JUST THE DIET
FOOD & WELLNESS DAILY LOG

Date: _____ Test Day #_____

Circle your suspected problem foods.
Common allergens: citrus, coffee, corn, dairy,
eggs, fish/shellfish, gluten, meat (beef, lamb,
pork), peanuts, raw fruits & vegetables, soy,
tree nuts

WHAT DID YOU EAT TODAY?

Meal #1, Time/Location _____
_____
_____
_____

Snack #1, Time/Location _____
_____
_____

Meal #2, Time/Location _____
_____
_____
_____

Snack #2, Time/Location _____
_____
_____

Meal #3, Time/Location _____
_____
_____
_____

Snack #3, Time/Location _____
_____

HOW DO YOU FEEL?
(Include Symptom/Time)
_____
_____
_____
_____
_____
_____
_____
_____
_____
_____
_____
_____
_____
_____
_____
_____
_____
_____
_____
_____
_____
_____
_____
_____
_____
_____
_____
_____
_____
_____
_____
_____

EXERCISE: What exercise did you do today?
How long? How do you feel?
_____
_____
_____

WATER: Cross off each 8-ounce glass of water
you drank today. (Mark other beverages with
meals.)

1   2   3   4   5   6   7   8   9   10

LAST NIGHT'S SLEEP

When did you fall asleep last night? _____

When did you wake this morning? _____

How well did you sleep last night? (Rate from 1-10, with 10 being best) _____

Comments about sleep

_____
_____
_____
_____
_____
_____
_____
_____
_____
_____
_____
_____
_____
_____
_____
_____
_____
_____
_____
_____

NEW MEDICATIONS/VITAMINS: List new medications. What side effects did you observe?

_____
_____
_____
_____
_____
_____
_____
_____
_____
_____
_____
_____
_____
_____

VITALS

Blood Sugar/Time _____ / _____
Blood Sugar/Time _____ / _____

Blood Pressure/Time _____ / _____
Blood Pressure/Time _____ / _____

Weight _____

BOWEL MOVEMENTS

BM No. 1/Time_____
BM Type (Circle) 1   2   3   4   5   6   7

Observations: _____
_____
_____

BM No. 2/Time_____
BM Type (Circle) 1   2   3   4   5   6   7

Observations: _____
_____
_____

BM No. 3/Time_____
BM Type (Circle) 1   2   3   4   5   6   7

Observations: _____
_____
_____

What challenge did you overcome today?

_____
_____
_____

What are you grateful for?

_____
_____
_____

What's the best thing that happened today?

_____
_____
_____

IT AIN'T JUST THE DIET
FOOD & WELLNESS DAILY LOG

Date: _____ Test Day #_____

Circle your suspected problem foods.
Common allergens: citrus, coffee, corn, dairy, eggs, fish/shellfish, gluten, meat (beef, lamb, pork), peanuts, raw fruits & vegetables, soy, tree nuts

WHAT DID YOU EAT TODAY?

Meal #1, Time/Location _____
_____
_____
_____
_____

Snack #1, Time/Location _____
_____
_____

Meal #2, Time/Location _____
_____
_____
_____
_____

Snack #2, Time/Location _____
_____
_____

Meal #3, Time/Location _____
_____
_____
_____
_____

Snack #3, Time/Location _____
_____
_____

HOW DO YOU FEEL?
(Include Symptom/Time)
_____
_____
_____
_____
_____
_____
_____
_____
_____
_____
_____
_____
_____
_____
_____
_____
_____
_____
_____
_____
_____
_____
_____
_____
_____
_____
_____
_____
_____
_____
_____
_____
_____
_____
_____
_____

EXERCISE: What exercise did you do today? How long? How do you feel?
_____
_____
_____

WATER: Cross off each 8-ounce glass of water you drank today. (Mark other beverages with meals.)

1   2   3   4   5   6   7   8   9   10

LAST NIGHT'S SLEEP

When did you fall asleep last night? _____

When did you wake this morning? _____

How well did you sleep last night? (Rate from 1-10, with 10 being best) _____

Comments about sleep

_____
_____
_____
_____
_____
_____
_____
_____
_____
_____
_____
_____
_____
_____
_____
_____
_____

NEW MEDICATIONS/VITAMINS: List new medications. What side effects did you observe?

_____
_____
_____
_____
_____
_____
_____
_____
_____
_____
_____
_____
_____
_____
_____

VITALS
Blood Sugar/Time _____/_____
Blood Sugar/Time _____/_____

Blood Pressure/Time _____/_____
Blood Pressure/Time _____/_____

Weight _____

BOWEL MOVEMENTS

BM No. 1/Time_____
BM Type (Circle) 1   2   3   4   5   6   7

Observations: _____
_____
_____

BM No. 2/Time_____
BM Type (Circle) 1   2   3   4   5   6   7

Observations: _____
_____
_____

BM No. 3/Time_____
BM Type (Circle) 1   2   3   4   5   6   7

Observations: _____
_____
_____

What challenge did you overcome today?

_____
_____
_____
_____

What are you grateful for?

_____
_____
_____
_____

What's the best thing that happened today?

_____
_____
_____
_____

Food Allergies, Sensitivities, & Intolerances Symptoms Checklist

Week 3 Assessment

Date: _____

Check each symptom you have experienced after eating (currently or in the recent past).

Breathing
- ☐ Sneezing
- ☐ Stuffy nose/sinuses
- ☐ Congestion
- ☐ Runny nose
- ☐ Face pain
- ☐ Difficulty breathing
- ☐ Wheezing or asthma

Skin
- ☐ Hives
- ☐ Eczema or rash
- ☐ Dandruff
- ☐ Ticklishness
- ☐ Flushing
- ☐ Rosy cheeks or ears

Eyes
- ☐ Itchy eyes
- ☐ Dry eyes

Digestive
- ☐ Bloating
- ☐ Gas
- ☐ Constipated
- ☐ Diarrhea or loose stools
- ☐ More bowel movements
- ☐ Fewer bowel movements
- ☐ Abdominal cramping
- ☐ Stinky bowel movements
- ☐ Undigested food in stool
- ☐ Bloody stool

Brain/Thinking
- ☐ Brain fog
- ☐ Inability to concentrate
- ☐ Disjointed or distractible thinking
- ☐ Headaches
- ☐ Glassy-eyed or spacey
- ☐ Trouble remembering things

Energy
- ☐ Hyperactivity
- ☐ Restlessness
- ☐ Tiredness/fatigue
- ☐ Low energy/activity

Difference in Sleep
- ☐ Better
- ☐ Worse
- ☐ Restless leg while sleeping
- ☐ Ideas why? _____

Pain
- ☐ Joint pain
- ☐ Muscle pain
- ☐ Other pain: _____

Mood
- ☐ Ecstatic
- ☐ Happy
- ☐ Neutral
- ☐ Sad
- ☐ Angry/Irritable
- ☐ Calm
- ☐ Anxious
- ☐ Feeling stressed (hair on fire)
- ☐ Filled with creativity
- ☐ Exhausted/no energy

Hunger Changes
- ☐ Craving certain foods (list) _____
- ☐ Hungry all the time
- ☐ Little or no interest in food

Other
- ☐ Bad breath
- ☐ Stinky feet
- ☐ Sweating hands/feet
- ☐ Other: _____

Notes:
_____
_____
_____
_____
_____
_____
_____
_____
_____
_____
_____
_____

Week 3 Journal Prompt
What's your favorite food or recipe to cook? Why? How did you learn to cook it?

_____
_____
_____
_____
_____
_____
_____
_____
_____
_____
_____
_____
_____
_____
_____
_____
_____
_____
_____
_____
_____
_____
_____
_____
_____
_____
_____
_____
_____
_____
_____
_____

IT AIN'T JUST THE DIET
FOOD & WELLNESS DAILY LOG

Date: _____ Test Day #_____

Circle your suspected problem foods.
Common allergens: citrus, coffee, corn, dairy, eggs, fish/shellfish, gluten, meat (beef, lamb, pork), peanuts, raw fruits & vegetables, soy, tree nuts

WHAT DID YOU EAT TODAY?

Meal #1, Time/Location _____
_____
_____
_____

Snack #1, Time/Location _____
_____
_____

Meal #2, Time/Location _____
_____
_____
_____

Snack #2, Time/Location _____
_____
_____

Meal #3, Time/Location _____
_____
_____
_____

Snack #3, Time/Location _____
_____
_____

HOW DO YOU FEEL?
(Include Symptom/Time)
_____
_____
_____
_____
_____
_____
_____
_____
_____
_____
_____
_____
_____
_____
_____
_____
_____
_____
_____
_____
_____
_____
_____
_____
_____
_____
_____
_____
_____
_____
_____
_____
_____
_____
_____
_____

EXERCISE: What exercise did you do today? How long? How do you feel?
_____
_____
_____

WATER: Cross off each 8-ounce glass of water you drank today. (Mark other beverages with meals.)

1   2   3   4   5   6   7   8   9   10

LAST NIGHT'S SLEEP

When did you fall asleep last night? _____

When did you wake this morning? _____

How well did you sleep last night? (Rate from
1-10, with 10 being best) _____

Comments about sleep

_____
_____
_____
_____
_____
_____
_____
_____
_____
_____
_____
_____
_____
_____
_____
_____
_____
_____

NEW MEDICATIONS/VITAMINS: List new
medications. What side effects did you
observe?

_____
_____
_____
_____
_____
_____
_____
_____
_____
_____
_____
_____
_____
_____
_____

VITALS

Blood Sugar/Time _____/_____
Blood Sugar/Time _____/_____

Blood Pressure/Time _____/_____
Blood Pressure/Time _____/_____

Weight _____

BOWEL MOVEMENTS

BM No. 1/Time_____
BM Type (Circle) 1 2 3 4 5 6 7

Observations: _____
_____
_____

BM No. 2/Time_____
BM Type (Circle) 1 2 3 4 5 6 7

Observations: _____
_____
_____

BM No. 3/Time_____
BM Type (Circle) 1 2 3 4 5 6 7

Observations: _____
_____
_____

What challenge did you overcome today?

_____
_____
_____

What are you grateful for?

_____
_____
_____

What's the best thing that happened today?

_____
_____
_____

IT AIN'T JUST THE DIET
FOOD & WELLNESS DAILY LOG

Date: _____ Test Day #_____

Circle your suspected problem foods.
Common allergens: citrus, coffee, corn, dairy,
eggs, fish/shellfish, gluten, meat (beef, lamb,
pork), peanuts, raw fruits & vegetables, soy,
tree nuts

WHAT DID YOU EAT TODAY?

Meal #1, Time/Location _____
_____
_____
_____

Snack #1, Time/Location _____
_____
_____

Meal #2, Time/Location _____
_____
_____
_____

Snack #2, Time/Location _____
_____
_____

Meal #3, Time/Location _____
_____
_____
_____

Snack #3, Time/Location _____
_____
_____

HOW DO YOU FEEL?
(Include Symptom/Time)
_____
_____
_____
_____
_____
_____
_____
_____
_____
_____
_____
_____
_____
_____
_____
_____
_____
_____
_____
_____
_____
_____
_____
_____
_____
_____
_____
_____
_____
_____
_____
_____

EXERCISE: What exercise did you do today?
How long? How do you feel?
_____
_____
_____

WATER: Cross off each 8-ounce glass of water
you drank today. (Mark other beverages with
meals.)

1   2   3   4   5   6   7   8   9   10

LAST NIGHT'S SLEEP

When did you fall asleep last night? _____

When did you wake this morning? _____

How well did you sleep last night? (Rate from 1-10, with 10 being best) _____

Comments about sleep

_____
_____
_____
_____
_____
_____
_____
_____
_____
_____
_____
_____
_____
_____
_____
_____
_____
_____

NEW MEDICATIONS/VITAMINS: List new medications. What side effects did you observe?

_____
_____
_____
_____
_____
_____
_____
_____
_____
_____
_____
_____
_____

VITALS

Blood Sugar/Time _____/_____
Blood Sugar/Time _____/_____

Blood Pressure/Time _____/_____
Blood Pressure/Time _____/_____

Weight _____

BOWEL MOVEMENTS

BM No. 1/Time_____
BM Type (Circle) 1   2   3   4   5   6   7

Observations: _____
_____
_____

BM No. 2/Time_____
BM Type (Circle) 1   2   3   4   5   6   7

Observations: _____
_____
_____

BM No. 3/Time_____
BM Type (Circle) 1   2   3   4   5   6   7

Observations: _____
_____
_____

What challenge did you overcome today?
_____
_____
_____

What are you grateful for?
_____
_____
_____

What's the best thing that happened today?
_____
_____
_____

IT AIN'T JUST THE DIET
FOOD & WELLNESS DAILY LOG

Date: _____ Test Day #_____

Circle your suspected problem foods.
Common allergens: citrus, coffee, corn, dairy, eggs, fish/shellfish, gluten, meat (beef, lamb, pork), peanuts, raw fruits & vegetables, soy, tree nuts

WHAT DID YOU EAT TODAY?

Meal #1, Time/Location _____
_____
_____
_____

Snack #1, Time/Location _____
_____
_____

Meal #2, Time/Location _____
_____
_____
_____

Snack #2, Time/Location _____
_____
_____

Meal #3, Time/Location _____
_____
_____
_____

Snack #3, Time/Location _____
_____
_____

HOW DO YOU FEEL?
(Include Symptom/Time)
_____
_____
_____
_____
_____
_____
_____
_____
_____
_____
_____
_____
_____
_____
_____
_____
_____
_____
_____
_____
_____
_____
_____
_____
_____
_____
_____
_____
_____
_____
_____
_____
_____
_____

EXERCISE: What exercise did you do today? How long? How do you feel?
_____
_____
_____

WATER: Cross off each 8-ounce glass of water you drank today. (Mark other beverages with meals.)

1   2   3   4   5   6   7   8   9   10

LAST NIGHT'S SLEEP

When did you fall asleep last night? _____

When did you wake this morning? _____

How well did you sleep last night? (Rate from 1-10, with 10 being best) _____

Comments about sleep

_____
_____
_____
_____
_____
_____
_____
_____
_____
_____
_____
_____
_____
_____
_____
_____
_____
_____

NEW MEDICATIONS/VITAMINS: List new medications. What side effects did you observe?

_____
_____
_____
_____
_____
_____
_____
_____
_____
_____
_____
_____
_____
_____

VITALS

Blood Sugar/Time _____/_____
Blood Sugar/Time _____/_____

Blood Pressure/Time _____/_____
Blood Pressure/Time _____/_____

Weight _____

BOWEL MOVEMENTS

BM No. 1/Time_____
BM Type (Circle) 1 2 3 4 5 6 7

Observations: _____
_____
_____

BM No. 2/Time_____
BM Type (Circle) 1 2 3 4 5 6 7

Observations: _____
_____
_____

BM No. 3/Time_____
BM Type (Circle) 1 2 3 4 5 6 7

Observations: _____
_____
_____

What challenge did you overcome today?

_____
_____
_____

What are you grateful for?

_____
_____
_____

What's the best thing that happened today?

_____
_____
_____

IT AIN'T JUST THE DIET
FOOD & WELLNESS DAILY LOG

Date: _____ Test Day #_____

Circle your suspected problem foods.
Common allergens: citrus, coffee, corn, dairy, eggs, fish/shellfish, gluten, meat (beef, lamb, pork), peanuts, raw fruits & vegetables, soy, tree nuts

WHAT DID YOU EAT TODAY?

Meal #1, Time/Location _____
_____
_____
_____

Snack #1, Time/Location _____
_____
_____

Meal #2, Time/Location _____
_____
_____
_____

Snack #2, Time/Location _____
_____
_____

Meal #3, Time/Location _____
_____
_____
_____

Snack #3, Time/Location _____
_____
_____

HOW DO YOU FEEL?
(Include Symptom/Time)
_____
_____
_____
_____
_____
_____
_____
_____
_____
_____
_____
_____
_____
_____
_____
_____
_____
_____
_____
_____
_____
_____
_____
_____
_____
_____
_____
_____
_____
_____
_____
_____
_____

EXERCISE: What exercise did you do today? How long? How do you feel?
_____
_____
_____

WATER: Cross off each 8-ounce glass of water you drank today. (Mark other beverages with meals.)

1   2   3   4   5   6   7   8   9   10

LAST NIGHT'S SLEEP

When did you fall asleep last night? _____

When did you wake this morning? _____

How well did you sleep last night? (Rate from
1-10, with 10 being best) _____

Comments about sleep

_____
_____
_____
_____
_____
_____
_____
_____
_____
_____
_____
_____
_____
_____
_____
_____
_____
_____

NEW MEDICATIONS/VITAMINS: List new
medications. What side effects did you
observe?

_____
_____
_____
_____
_____
_____
_____
_____
_____
_____
_____
_____
_____

VITALS
Blood Sugar/Time _____/_____
Blood Sugar/Time _____/_____

Blood Pressure/Time _____/_____
Blood Pressure/Time _____/_____

Weight _____

BOWEL MOVEMENTS

BM No. 1/Time_____
BM Type (Circle) 1   2   3   4   5   6   7

Observations: _____
_____
_____

BM No. 2/Time_____
BM Type (Circle) 1   2   3   4   5   6   7

Observations: _____
_____
_____

BM No. 3/Time_____
BM Type (Circle) 1   2   3   4   5   6   7

Observations: _____
_____
_____

What challenge did you overcome today?
_____
_____
_____
_____

What are you grateful for?
_____
_____
_____

What's the best thing that happened today?
_____
_____
_____

IT AIN'T JUST THE DIET
FOOD & WELLNESS DAILY LOG

Date: _____ Test Day #_____

Circle your suspected problem foods.
Common allergens: citrus, coffee, corn, dairy, eggs, fish/shellfish, gluten, meat (beef, lamb, pork), peanuts, raw fruits & vegetables, soy, tree nuts

WHAT DID YOU EAT TODAY?

Meal #1, Time/Location _____
_____
_____
_____

Snack #1, Time/Location _____
_____
_____

Meal #2, Time/Location _____
_____
_____
_____

Snack #2, Time/Location _____
_____
_____

Meal #3, Time/Location _____
_____
_____
_____

Snack #3, Time/Location _____
_____
_____

HOW DO YOU FEEL?
(Include Symptom/Time)
_____
_____
_____
_____
_____
_____
_____
_____
_____
_____
_____
_____
_____
_____
_____
_____
_____
_____
_____
_____
_____
_____
_____
_____
_____
_____
_____
_____
_____
_____
_____
_____

EXERCISE: What exercise did you do today? How long? How do you feel?
_____
_____
_____

WATER: Cross off each 8-ounce glass of water you drank today. (Mark other beverages with meals.)

1   2   3   4   5   6   7   8   9   10

LAST NIGHT'S SLEEP

When did you fall asleep last night? _____

When did you wake this morning? _____

How well did you sleep last night? (Rate from 1-10, with 10 being best) _____

Comments about sleep

_____
_____
_____
_____
_____
_____
_____
_____
_____
_____
_____
_____
_____
_____
_____
_____
_____
_____

NEW MEDICATIONS/VITAMINS: List new medications. What side effects did you observe?

_____
_____
_____
_____
_____
_____
_____
_____
_____
_____
_____
_____
_____
_____

VITALS

Blood Sugar/Time _____/_____

Blood Sugar/Time _____/_____

Blood Pressure/Time _____/_____

Blood Pressure/Time _____/_____

Weight _____

BOWEL MOVEMENTS

BM No. 1/Time_____

BM Type (Circle) 1   2   3   4   5   6   7

Observations: _____
_____
_____

BM No. 2/Time_____

BM Type (Circle) 1   2   3   4   5   6   7

Observations: _____
_____
_____

BM No. 3/Time_____

BM Type (Circle) 1   2   3   4   5   6   7

Observations: _____
_____
_____

What challenge did you overcome today?

_____
_____
_____

What are you grateful for?

_____
_____
_____

What's the best thing that happened today?

_____
_____
_____

IT AIN'T JUST THE DIET
FOOD & WELLNESS DAILY LOG

Date: _____ Test Day #_____

Circle your suspected problem foods.
Common allergens: citrus, coffee, corn, dairy, eggs, fish/shellfish, gluten, meat (beef, lamb, pork), peanuts, raw fruits & vegetables, soy, tree nuts

WHAT DID YOU EAT TODAY?

Meal #1, Time/Location _____
_____
_____
_____
_____

Snack #1, Time/Location _____
_____
_____

Meal #2, Time/Location _____
_____
_____
_____
_____

Snack #2, Time/Location _____
_____
_____

Meal #3, Time/Location _____
_____
_____
_____
_____

Snack #3, Time/Location _____
_____
_____

HOW DO YOU FEEL?
(Include Symptom/Time)

_____
_____
_____
_____
_____
_____
_____
_____
_____
_____
_____
_____
_____
_____
_____
_____
_____
_____
_____
_____
_____
_____
_____
_____
_____
_____
_____
_____
_____
_____
_____
_____
_____
_____
_____

EXERCISE: What exercise did you do today? How long? How do you feel?
_____
_____
_____

WATER: Cross off each 8-ounce glass of water you drank today. (Mark other beverages with meals.)

1   2   3   4   5   6   7   8   9   10

LAST NIGHT'S SLEEP

When did you fall asleep last night? _____

When did you wake this morning? _____

How well did you sleep last night? (Rate from 1-10, with 10 being best) _____

Comments about sleep

_____
_____
_____
_____
_____
_____
_____
_____
_____
_____
_____
_____
_____
_____
_____
_____
_____
_____

NEW MEDICATIONS/VITAMINS: List new medications. What side effects did you observe?

_____
_____
_____
_____
_____
_____
_____
_____
_____
_____
_____
_____
_____
_____
_____
_____

VITALS

Blood Sugar/Time _____/_____
Blood Sugar/Time _____/_____

Blood Pressure/Time _____/_____
Blood Pressure/Time _____/_____

Weight _____

BOWEL MOVEMENTS

BM No. 1/Time_____
BM Type (Circle) 1   2   3   4   5   6   7

Observations: _____
_____
_____

BM No. 2/Time_____
BM Type (Circle) 1   2   3   4   5   6   7

Observations: _____
_____
_____

BM No. 3/Time_____
BM Type (Circle) 1   2   3   4   5   6   7

Observations: _____
_____
_____

What challenge did you overcome today?

_____
_____
_____

What are you grateful for?

_____
_____
_____

What's the best thing that happened today?

_____
_____
_____

IT AIN'T JUST THE DIET
FOOD & WELLNESS DAILY LOG

Date: _____ Test Day #_____

Circle your suspected problem foods.
Common allergens: citrus, coffee, corn, dairy, eggs, fish/shellfish, gluten, meat (beef, lamb, pork), peanuts, raw fruits & vegetables, soy, tree nuts

WHAT DID YOU EAT TODAY?

Meal #1, Time/Location _____
_____
_____
_____
_____

Snack #1, Time/Location _____
_____
_____

Meal #2, Time/Location _____
_____
_____
_____
_____

Snack #2, Time/Location _____
_____
_____

Meal #3, Time/Location _____
_____
_____
_____
_____

Snack #3, Time/Location _____
_____
_____

HOW DO YOU FEEL?
(Include Symptom/Time)
_____
_____
_____
_____
_____
_____
_____
_____
_____
_____
_____
_____
_____
_____
_____
_____
_____
_____
_____
_____
_____
_____
_____
_____
_____
_____
_____
_____
_____
_____
_____
_____
_____
_____
_____

EXERCISE: What exercise did you do today? How long? How do you feel?
_____
_____
_____

WATER: Cross off each 8-ounce glass of water you drank today. (Mark other beverages with meals.)

1   2   3   4   5   6   7   8   9   10

LAST NIGHT'S SLEEP

When did you fall asleep last night? _____

When did you wake this morning? _____

How well did you sleep last night? (Rate from 1-10, with 10 being best) _____

Comments about sleep

_____
_____
_____
_____
_____
_____
_____
_____
_____
_____
_____
_____
_____
_____
_____
_____
_____
_____
_____

NEW MEDICATIONS/VITAMINS: List new medications. What side effects did you observe?

_____
_____
_____
_____
_____
_____
_____
_____
_____
_____
_____
_____
_____

VITALS

Blood Sugar/Time _____/_____
Blood Sugar/Time _____/_____

Blood Pressure/Time _____/_____
Blood Pressure/Time _____/_____

Weight _____

BOWEL MOVEMENTS

BM No. 1/Time_____
BM Type (Circle) 1   2   3   4   5   6   7

Observations: _____
_____
_____

BM No. 2/Time_____
BM Type (Circle) 1   2   3   4   5   6   7

Observations: _____
_____
_____

BM No. 3/Time_____
BM Type (Circle) 1   2   3   4   5   6   7

Observations: _____
_____
_____

What challenge did you overcome today?
_____
_____
_____
_____

What are you grateful for?
_____
_____
_____
_____

What's the best thing that happened today?
_____
_____
_____
_____

Food Allergies, Sensitivities, & Intolerances Symptoms Checklist

Week 4 Assessment

Date: _____

Check each symptom you have experienced after eating (currently or in the recent past).

Breathing
- ☐ Sneezing
- ☐ Stuffy nose/sinuses
- ☐ Congestion
- ☐ Runny nose
- ☐ Face pain
- ☐ Difficulty breathing
- ☐ Wheezing or asthma

Skin
- ☐ Hives
- ☐ Eczema or rash
- ☐ Dandruff
- ☐ Ticklishness
- ☐ Flushing
- ☐ Rosy cheeks or ears

Eyes
- ☐ Itchy eyes
- ☐ Dry eyes

Digestive
- ☐ Bloating
- ☐ Gas
- ☐ Constipated
- ☐ Diarrhea or loose stools
- ☐ More bowel movements
- ☐ Fewer bowel movements
- ☐ Abdominal cramping
- ☐ Stinky bowel movements
- ☐ Undigested food in stool
- ☐ Bloody stool

Brain/Thinking
- ☐ Brain fog
- ☐ Inability to concentrate
- ☐ Disjointed or distractible thinking
- ☐ Headaches
- ☐ Glassy-eyed or spacey
- ☐ Trouble remembering things

Energy
- ☐ Hyperactivity
- ☐ Restlessness
- ☐ Tiredness/fatigue
- ☐ Low energy/activity

Difference in Sleep
- ☐ Better
- ☐ Worse
- ☐ Restless leg while sleeping
- ☐ Ideas why? _____

Pain
- ☐ Joint pain
- ☐ Muscle pain
- ☐ Other pain: _____

Mood
- ☐ Ecstatic
- ☐ Happy
- ☐ Neutral
- ☐ Sad
- ☐ Angry/Irritable
- ☐ Calm
- ☐ Anxious
- ☐ Feeling stressed (hair on fire)
- ☐ Filled with creativity
- ☐ Exhausted/no energy

Hunger Changes
- ☐ Craving certain foods (list) _____
- ☐ Hungry all the time
- ☐ Little or no interest in food

Other
- ☐ Bad breath
- ☐ Stinky feet
- ☐ Sweating hands/feet
- ☐ Other: _____

Notes:

_____
_____
_____
_____
_____
_____
_____
_____
_____
_____
_____

Week 4 Journal Prompt

How can you enlist the help and support of friends and family so you
can continue to become healthier?

_____
_____
_____
_____
_____
_____
_____
_____
_____
_____
_____
_____
_____
_____
_____
_____
_____
_____
_____
_____
_____
_____
_____
_____
_____
_____
_____
_____
_____

IT AIN'T JUST THE DIET
FOOD & WELLNESS DAILY LOG

Date: _____ Test Day #_____

Circle your suspected problem foods.
Common allergens: citrus, coffee, corn, dairy, eggs, fish/shellfish, gluten, meat (beef, lamb, pork), peanuts, raw fruits & vegetables, soy, tree nuts

WHAT DID YOU EAT TODAY?

Meal #1, Time/Location _____
_____
_____
_____

Snack #1, Time/Location _____
_____
_____

Meal #2, Time/Location _____
_____
_____
_____

Snack #2, Time/Location _____
_____
_____

Meal #3, Time/Location _____
_____
_____
_____

Snack #3, Time/Location _____
_____

HOW DO YOU FEEL?
(Include Symptom/Time)
_____
_____
_____
_____
_____
_____
_____
_____
_____
_____
_____
_____
_____
_____
_____
_____
_____
_____
_____
_____
_____
_____
_____
_____
_____
_____
_____
_____
_____
_____
_____
_____
_____

EXERCISE: What exercise did you do today? How long? How do you feel?
_____
_____
_____

WATER: Cross off each 8-ounce glass of water you drank today. (Mark other beverages with meals.)

1   2   3   4   5   6   7   8   9   10

LAST NIGHT'S SLEEP

When did you fall asleep last night? _____

When did you wake this morning? _____

How well did you sleep last night? (Rate from 1-10, with 10 being best) _____

Comments about sleep

_____
_____
_____
_____
_____
_____
_____
_____
_____
_____
_____
_____
_____
_____
_____
_____
_____
_____
_____

NEW MEDICATIONS/VITAMINS: List new medications. What side effects did you observe?

_____
_____
_____
_____
_____
_____
_____
_____
_____
_____
_____
_____
_____
_____

VITALS

Blood Sugar/Time _____/_____
Blood Sugar/Time _____/_____

Blood Pressure/Time _____/_____
Blood Pressure/Time _____/_____

Weight _____

BOWEL MOVEMENTS

BM No. 1/Time_____
BM Type (Circle) 1   2   3   4   5   6   7

Observations: _____
_____
_____

BM No. 2/Time_____
BM Type (Circle) 1   2   3   4   5   6   7

Observations: _____
_____
_____

BM No. 3/Time_____
BM Type (Circle) 1   2   3   4   5   6   7

Observations: _____
_____
_____

What challenge did you overcome today?

_____
_____
_____

What are you grateful for?

_____
_____
_____

What's the best thing that happened today?

_____
_____
_____

IT AIN'T JUST THE DIET
FOOD & WELLNESS DAILY LOG

Date: _____ Test Day #_____

Circle your suspected problem foods.
Common allergens: citrus, coffee, corn, dairy, eggs, fish/shellfish, gluten, meat (beef, lamb, pork), peanuts, raw fruits & vegetables, soy, tree nuts

WHAT DID YOU EAT TODAY?

Meal #1, Time/Location _____
_____
_____
_____

Snack #1, Time/Location _____
_____

Meal #2, Time/Location _____
_____
_____
_____

Snack #2, Time/Location _____
_____

Meal #3, Time/Location _____
_____
_____
_____

Snack #3, Time/Location _____
_____

HOW DO YOU FEEL?
(Include Symptom/Time)
_____
_____
_____
_____
_____
_____
_____
_____
_____
_____
_____
_____
_____
_____
_____
_____
_____
_____
_____
_____
_____
_____
_____
_____
_____
_____
_____
_____
_____
_____
_____

EXERCISE: What exercise did you do today? How long? How do you feel?
_____
_____
_____

WATER: Cross off each 8-ounce glass of water you drank today. (Mark other beverages with meals.)

1   2   3   4   5   6   7   8   9   10

LAST NIGHT'S SLEEP

When did you fall asleep last night? _____

When did you wake this morning? _____

How well did you sleep last night? (Rate from 1-10, with 10 being best) _____

Comments about sleep

_____
_____
_____
_____
_____
_____
_____
_____
_____
_____
_____
_____
_____
_____
_____
_____
_____
_____
_____

NEW MEDICATIONS/VITAMINS: List new medications. What side effects did you observe?

_____
_____
_____
_____
_____
_____
_____
_____
_____
_____
_____
_____
_____
_____
_____
_____

VITALS

Blood Sugar/Time _____/_____
Blood Sugar/Time _____/_____

Blood Pressure/Time _____/_____
Blood Pressure/Time _____/_____

Weight _____

BOWEL MOVEMENTS

BM No. 1/Time_____
BM Type (Circle) 1   2   3   4   5   6   7

Observations: _____
_____
_____

BM No. 2/Time_____
BM Type (Circle) 1   2   3   4   5   6   7

Observations: _____
_____
_____

BM No. 3/Time_____
BM Type (Circle) 1   2   3   4   5   6   7

Observations: _____
_____
_____

What challenge did you overcome today?
_____
_____
_____

What are you grateful for?
_____
_____
_____

What's the best thing that happened today?
_____
_____
_____

IT AIN'T JUST THE DIET
FOOD & WELLNESS DAILY LOG

Date: _____ Test Day #_____

Circle your suspected problem foods.
Common allergens: citrus, coffee, corn, dairy, eggs, fish/shellfish, gluten, meat (beef, lamb, pork), peanuts, raw fruits & vegetables, soy, tree nuts

WHAT DID YOU EAT TODAY?

Meal #1, Time/Location _____
_____
_____
_____

Snack #1, Time/Location _____
_____
_____

Meal #2, Time/Location _____
_____
_____
_____

Snack #2, Time/Location _____
_____
_____

Meal #3, Time/Location _____
_____
_____
_____

Snack #3, Time/Location _____
_____
_____

HOW DO YOU FEEL?
(Include Symptom/Time)
_____
_____
_____
_____
_____
_____
_____
_____
_____
_____
_____
_____
_____
_____
_____
_____
_____
_____
_____
_____
_____
_____
_____
_____
_____
_____
_____
_____
_____
_____
_____
_____
_____

EXERCISE: What exercise did you do today? How long? How do you feel?
_____
_____
_____

WATER: Cross off each 8-ounce glass of water you drank today. (Mark other beverages with meals.)

1   2   3   4   5   6   7   8   9   10

LAST NIGHT'S SLEEP

When did you fall asleep last night? _____

When did you wake this morning? _____

How well did you sleep last night? (Rate from 1-10, with 10 being best) _____

Comments about sleep

_____
_____
_____
_____
_____
_____
_____
_____
_____
_____
_____
_____
_____
_____
_____
_____
_____
_____
_____
_____

NEW MEDICATIONS/VITAMINS: List new medications. What side effects did you observe?

_____
_____
_____
_____
_____
_____
_____
_____
_____
_____
_____
_____
_____
_____
_____
_____
_____

VITALS

Blood Sugar/Time _____/_____
Blood Sugar/Time _____/_____

Blood Pressure/Time _____/_____
Blood Pressure/Time _____/_____

Weight _____

BOWEL MOVEMENTS

BM No. 1/Time_____
BM Type (Circle) 1   2   3   4   5   6   7

Observations: _____
_____
_____

BM No. 2/Time_____
BM Type (Circle) 1   2   3   4   5   6   7

Observations: _____
_____
_____

BM No. 3/Time_____
BM Type (Circle) 1   2   3   4   5   6   7

Observations: _____
_____
_____

What challenge did you overcome today?

_____
_____
_____

What are you grateful for?

_____
_____
_____

What's the best thing that happened today?

_____
_____
_____

IT AIN'T JUST THE DIET
FOOD & WELLNESS DAILY LOG

Date: _____ Test Day #_____

Circle your suspected problem foods.
Common allergens: citrus, coffee, corn, dairy, eggs, fish/shellfish, gluten, meat (beef, lamb, pork), peanuts, raw fruits & vegetables, soy, tree nuts

WHAT DID YOU EAT TODAY?

Meal #1, Time/Location _____
_____
_____
_____

Snack #1, Time/Location _____
_____
_____

Meal #2, Time/Location _____
_____
_____
_____

Snack #2, Time/Location _____
_____
_____

Meal #3, Time/Location _____
_____
_____
_____

Snack #3, Time/Location _____
_____
_____

HOW DO YOU FEEL?
(Include Symptom/Time)
_____
_____
_____
_____
_____
_____
_____
_____
_____
_____
_____
_____
_____
_____
_____
_____
_____
_____
_____
_____
_____
_____
_____
_____
_____
_____
_____
_____
_____
_____
_____
_____
_____
_____
_____
_____
_____

EXERCISE: What exercise did you do today? How long? How do you feel?
_____
_____
_____

WATER: Cross off each 8-ounce glass of water you drank today. (Mark other beverages with meals.)

1   2   3   4   5   6   7   8   9   10

LAST NIGHT'S SLEEP

When did you fall asleep last night? _____

When did you wake this morning? _____

How well did you sleep last night? (Rate from 1-10, with 10 being best) _____

Comments about sleep

_____
_____
_____
_____
_____
_____
_____
_____
_____
_____
_____
_____
_____
_____
_____
_____
_____
_____
_____

NEW MEDICATIONS/VITAMINS: List new medications. What side effects did you observe?

_____
_____
_____
_____
_____
_____
_____
_____
_____
_____
_____
_____
_____
_____
_____

VITALS

Blood Sugar/Time _____/_____
Blood Sugar/Time _____/_____

Blood Pressure/Time _____/_____
Blood Pressure/Time _____/_____

Weight _____

BOWEL MOVEMENTS

BM No. 1/Time_____
BM Type (Circle) 1   2   3   4   5   6   7

Observations: _____
_____
_____

BM No. 2/Time_____
BM Type (Circle) 1   2   3   4   5   6   7

Observations: _____
_____
_____

BM No. 3/Time_____
BM Type (Circle) 1   2   3   4   5   6   7

Observations: _____
_____
_____

What challenge did you overcome today?
_____
_____
_____

What are you grateful for?
_____
_____
_____

What's the best thing that happened today?
_____
_____
_____

IT AIN'T JUST THE DIET
FOOD & WELLNESS DAILY LOG

Date: _____ Test Day #_____

Circle your suspected problem foods.
Common allergens: citrus, coffee, corn, dairy, eggs, fish/shellfish, gluten, meat (beef, lamb, pork), peanuts, raw fruits & vegetables, soy, tree nuts

WHAT DID YOU EAT TODAY?

Meal #1, Time/Location _____
_____
_____
_____

Snack #1, Time/Location _____
_____
_____

Meal #2, Time/Location _____
_____
_____
_____

Snack #2, Time/Location _____
_____
_____

Meal #3, Time/Location _____
_____
_____
_____

Snack #3, Time/Location _____
_____
_____

HOW DO YOU FEEL?
(Include Symptom/Time)
_____
_____
_____
_____
_____
_____
_____
_____
_____
_____
_____
_____
_____
_____
_____
_____
_____
_____
_____
_____
_____
_____
_____
_____
_____
_____
_____
_____
_____
_____
_____
_____

EXERCISE: What exercise did you do today? How long? How do you feel?
_____
_____
_____

WATER: Cross off each 8-ounce glass of water you drank today. (Mark other beverages with meals.)

1   2   3   4   5   6   7   8   9   10

LAST NIGHT'S SLEEP

When did you fall asleep last night? _____

When did you wake this morning? _____

How well did you sleep last night? (Rate from 1-10, with 10 being best) _____

Comments about sleep

_____
_____
_____
_____
_____
_____
_____
_____
_____
_____
_____
_____
_____
_____
_____
_____
_____
_____

NEW MEDICATIONS/VITAMINS: List new medications. What side effects did you observe?

_____
_____
_____
_____
_____
_____
_____
_____
_____
_____
_____
_____
_____
_____

VITALS

Blood Sugar/Time _____/_____
Blood Sugar/Time _____/_____

Blood Pressure/Time _____/_____
Blood Pressure/Time _____/_____

Weight _____

BOWEL MOVEMENTS

BM No. 1/Time_____
BM Type (Circle) 1   2   3   4   5   6   7

Observations: _____
_____
_____

BM No. 2/Time_____
BM Type (Circle) 1   2   3   4   5   6   7

Observations: _____
_____
_____

BM No. 3/Time_____
BM Type (Circle) 1   2   3   4   5   6   7

Observations: _____
_____
_____

What challenge did you overcome today?
_____
_____
_____

What are you grateful for?
_____
_____
_____

What's the best thing that happened today?
_____
_____
_____

IT AIN'T JUST THE DIET
FOOD & WELLNESS DAILY LOG

Date: _____ Test Day # _____

Circle your suspected problem foods.
Common allergens: citrus, coffee, corn, dairy, eggs, fish/shellfish, gluten, meat (beef, lamb, pork), peanuts, raw fruits & vegetables, soy, tree nuts

WHAT DID YOU EAT TODAY?

Meal #1, Time/Location _____
_____
_____
_____

Snack #1, Time/Location _____
_____
_____

Meal #2, Time/Location _____
_____
_____
_____

Snack #2, Time/Location _____
_____
_____

Meal #3, Time/Location _____
_____
_____
_____

Snack #3, Time/Location _____
_____

HOW DO YOU FEEL?
(Include Symptom/Time)
_____
_____
_____
_____
_____
_____
_____
_____
_____
_____
_____
_____
_____
_____
_____
_____
_____
_____
_____
_____
_____
_____
_____
_____
_____
_____
_____
_____
_____
_____
_____
_____
_____
_____
_____
_____
_____
_____

EXERCISE: What exercise did you do today? How long? How do you feel?
_____
_____
_____

WATER: Cross off each 8-ounce glass of water you drank today. (Mark other beverages with meals.)

1   2   3   4   5   6   7   8   9   10

LAST NIGHT'S SLEEP

When did you fall asleep last night? _____

When did you wake this morning? _____

How well did you sleep last night? (Rate from 1-10, with 10 being best) _____

Comments about sleep

_____
_____
_____
_____
_____
_____
_____
_____
_____
_____
_____
_____
_____
_____
_____
_____
_____
_____

NEW MEDICATIONS/VITAMINS: List new medications. What side effects did you observe?

_____
_____
_____
_____
_____
_____
_____
_____
_____
_____
_____
_____
_____

VITALS

Blood Sugar/Time _____/_____
Blood Sugar/Time _____/_____

Blood Pressure/Time _____/_____
Blood Pressure/Time _____/_____

Weight _____

BOWEL MOVEMENTS

BM No. 1/Time_____
BM Type (Circle) 1   2   3   4   5   6   7

Observations: _____
_____
_____

BM No. 2/Time_____
BM Type (Circle) 1   2   3   4   5   6   7

Observations: _____
_____
_____

BM No. 3/Time_____
BM Type (Circle) 1   2   3   4   5   6   7

Observations: _____
_____
_____

What challenge did you overcome today?

_____
_____
_____

What are you grateful for?

_____
_____
_____

What's the best thing that happened today?

_____
_____
_____

IT AIN'T JUST THE DIET
FOOD & WELLNESS DAILY LOG

Date: _____ Test Day #_____

Circle your suspected problem foods.
Common allergens: citrus, coffee, corn, dairy, eggs, fish/shellfish, gluten, meat (beef, lamb, pork), peanuts, raw fruits & vegetables, soy, tree nuts

WHAT DID YOU EAT TODAY?

Meal #1, Time/Location _____
_____
_____
_____

Snack #1, Time/Location _____
_____
_____

Meal #2, Time/Location _____
_____
_____
_____

Snack #2, Time/Location _____
_____
_____

Meal #3, Time/Location _____
_____
_____
_____

Snack #3, Time/Location _____
_____
_____

HOW DO YOU FEEL?
(Include Symptom/Time)
_____
_____
_____
_____
_____
_____
_____
_____
_____
_____
_____
_____
_____
_____
_____
_____
_____
_____
_____
_____
_____
_____
_____
_____
_____
_____
_____
_____
_____
_____
_____
_____
_____
_____
_____
_____
_____

EXERCISE: What exercise did you do today? How long? How do you feel?
_____
_____
_____

WATER: Cross off each 8-ounce glass of water you drank today. (Mark other beverages with meals.)

1   2   3   4   5   6   7   8   9   10

LAST NIGHT'S SLEEP

When did you fall asleep last night? _____

When did you wake this morning? _____

How well did you sleep last night? (Rate from
1-10, with 10 being best) _____

Comments about sleep

_____
_____
_____
_____
_____
_____
_____
_____
_____
_____
_____
_____
_____
_____
_____
_____

NEW MEDICATIONS/VITAMINS: List new
medications. What side effects did you
observe?

_____
_____
_____
_____
_____
_____
_____
_____
_____
_____
_____
_____
_____
_____

VITALS
Blood Sugar/Time _____/_____
Blood Sugar/Time _____/_____

Blood Pressure/Time _____/_____
Blood Pressure/Time _____/_____

Weight _____

BOWEL MOVEMENTS

BM No. 1/Time_____
BM Type (Circle) 1   2   3   4   5   6   7

Observations: _____
_____
_____

BM No. 2/Time_____
BM Type (Circle) 1   2   3   4   5   6   7

Observations: _____
_____
_____

BM No. 3/Time_____
BM Type (Circle) 1   2   3   4   5   6   7

Observations: _____
_____
_____

What challenge did you overcome today?

_____
_____
_____

What are you grateful for?

_____
_____
_____

What's the best thing that happened today?

_____
_____
_____

Food Allergies, Sensitivities, & Intolerances Symptoms Checklist

Week 5 Assessment

Date: _____

Check each symptom you have experienced after eating (currently or in the recent past).

Breathing
- ☐ Sneezing
- ☐ Stuffy nose/sinuses
- ☐ Congestion
- ☐ Runny nose
- ☐ Face pain
- ☐ Difficulty breathing
- ☐ Wheezing or asthma

Skin
- ☐ Hives
- ☐ Eczema or rash
- ☐ Dandruff
- ☐ Ticklishness
- ☐ Flushing
- ☐ Rosy cheeks or ears

Eyes
- ☐ Itchy eyes
- ☐ Dry eyes

Digestive
- ☐ Bloating
- ☐ Gas
- ☐ Constipated
- ☐ Diarrhea or loose stools
- ☐ More bowel movements
- ☐ Fewer bowel movements
- ☐ Abdominal cramping
- ☐ Stinky bowel movements
- ☐ Undigested food in stool
- ☐ Bloody stool

Brain/Thinking
- ☐ Brain fog
- ☐ Inability to concentrate
- ☐ Disjointed or distractible thinking
- ☐ Headaches
- ☐ Glassy-eyed or spacey
- ☐ Trouble remembering things

Energy
- ☐ Hyperactivity
- ☐ Restlessness
- ☐ Tiredness/fatigue
- ☐ Low energy/activity

Difference in Sleep
- ☐ Better
- ☐ Worse
- ☐ Restless leg while sleeping
- ☐ Ideas why? _____

Pain
- ☐ Joint pain
- ☐ Muscle pain
- ☐ Other pain: _____

Mood
- ☐ Ecstatic
- ☐ Happy
- ☐ Neutral
- ☐ Sad
- ☐ Angry/Irritable
- ☐ Calm
- ☐ Anxious
- ☐ Feeling stressed (hair on fire)
- ☐ Filled with creativity
- ☐ Exhausted/no energy

Hunger Changes
- ☐ Craving certain foods (list) _____
- ☐ Hungry all the time
- ☐ Little or no interest in food

Other
- ☐ Bad breath
- ☐ Stinky feet
- ☐ Sweating hands/feet
- ☐ Other: _____

Notes:
_____
_____
_____
_____
_____
_____
_____
_____
_____
_____
_____

Week 5 Journal Prompt

What can you do to make your life easier to help you avoid foods that cause problems for you?

_____

_____

_____

_____

_____

_____

_____

_____

_____

_____

_____

_____

_____

_____

_____

_____

_____

_____

_____

_____

_____

_____

_____

_____

_____

_____

_____

_____

_____

_____

_____

_____

IT AIN'T JUST THE DIET
FOOD & WELLNESS DAILY LOG

Date: _____ Test Day #_____

Circle your suspected problem foods.
Common allergens: citrus, coffee, corn, dairy,
eggs, fish/shellfish, gluten, meat (beef, lamb,
pork), peanuts, raw fruits & vegetables, soy,
tree nuts

WHAT DID YOU EAT TODAY?

Meal #1, Time/Location _____
_____
_____
_____

Snack #1, Time/Location _____
_____
_____

Meal #2, Time/Location _____
_____
_____
_____

Snack #2, Time/Location _____
_____
_____

Meal #3, Time/Location _____
_____
_____
_____

Snack #3, Time/Location _____
_____
_____

HOW DO YOU FEEL?
(Include Symptom/Time)
_____
_____
_____
_____
_____
_____
_____
_____
_____
_____
_____
_____
_____
_____
_____
_____
_____
_____
_____
_____
_____
_____
_____
_____
_____
_____
_____
_____
_____
_____
_____
_____

EXERCISE: What exercise did you do today?
How long? How do you feel?
_____
_____
_____

WATER: Cross off each 8-ounce glass of water
you drank today. (Mark other beverages with
meals.)

1   2   3   4   5   6   7   8   9   10

LAST NIGHT'S SLEEP

When did you fall asleep last night? _____

When did you wake this morning? _____

How well did you sleep last night? (Rate from 1-10, with 10 being best) _____

Comments about sleep

_____
_____
_____
_____
_____
_____
_____
_____
_____
_____
_____
_____
_____
_____
_____
_____
_____
_____
_____
_____
_____
_____

NEW MEDICATIONS/VITAMINS: List new medications. What side effects did you observe?

_____
_____
_____
_____
_____
_____
_____
_____
_____
_____
_____
_____
_____
_____
_____

VITALS

Blood Sugar/Time _____/_____
Blood Sugar/Time _____/_____

Blood Pressure/Time _____/_____
Blood Pressure/Time _____/_____

Weight _____

BOWEL MOVEMENTS

BM No. 1/Time_____
BM Type (Circle) 1   2   3   4   5   6   7

Observations: _____
_____
_____

BM No. 2/Time_____
BM Type (Circle) 1   2   3   4   5   6   7

Observations: _____
_____
_____

BM No. 3/Time_____
BM Type (Circle) 1   2   3   4   5   6   7

Observations: _____
_____
_____

What challenge did you overcome today?

_____
_____
_____
_____

What are you grateful for?

_____
_____
_____

What's the best thing that happened today?

_____
_____
_____

IT AIN'T JUST THE DIET
FOOD & WELLNESS DAILY LOG

Date: _____ Test Day #_____

Circle your suspected problem foods.
Common allergens: citrus, coffee, corn, dairy, eggs, fish/shellfish, gluten, meat (beef, lamb, pork), peanuts, raw fruits & vegetables, soy, tree nuts

WHAT DID YOU EAT TODAY?

Meal #1, Time/Location _____
_____
_____
_____

Snack #1, Time/Location _____
_____
_____

Meal #2, Time/Location _____
_____
_____
_____

Snack #2, Time/Location _____
_____
_____

Meal #3, Time/Location _____
_____
_____
_____

Snack #3, Time/Location _____
_____
_____

EXERCISE: What exercise did you do today? How long? How do you feel?
_____
_____

HOW DO YOU FEEL?
(Include Symptom/Time)
_____
_____
_____
_____
_____
_____
_____
_____
_____
_____
_____
_____
_____
_____
_____
_____
_____
_____
_____
_____
_____
_____
_____
_____
_____
_____
_____
_____
_____
_____
_____
_____
_____
_____
_____
_____

WATER: Cross off each 8-ounce glass of water you drank today. (Mark other beverages with meals.)

1   2   3   4   5   6   7   8   9   10

LAST NIGHT'S SLEEP

When did you fall asleep last night? _____

When did you wake this morning? _____

How well did you sleep last night? (Rate from 1-10, with 10 being best) _____

Comments about sleep

_____
_____
_____
_____
_____
_____
_____
_____
_____
_____
_____
_____
_____
_____
_____
_____
_____
_____

NEW MEDICATIONS/VITAMINS: List new medications. What side effects did you observe?

_____
_____
_____
_____
_____
_____
_____
_____
_____
_____
_____
_____
_____
_____

VITALS

Blood Sugar/Time _____/_____
Blood Sugar/Time _____/_____

Blood Pressure/Time _____/_____
Blood Pressure/Time _____/_____

Weight _____

BOWEL MOVEMENTS

BM No. 1/Time_____
BM Type (Circle) 1   2   3   4   5   6   7

Observations: _____
_____
_____

BM No. 2/Time_____
BM Type (Circle) 1   2   3   4   5   6   7

Observations: _____
_____
_____

BM No. 3/Time_____
BM Type (Circle) 1   2   3   4   5   6   7

Observations: _____
_____
_____

What challenge did you overcome today?

_____
_____
_____

What are you grateful for?

_____
_____
_____

What's the best thing that happened today?

_____
_____
_____

IT AIN'T JUST THE DIET
FOOD & WELLNESS DAILY LOG

Date: _____ Test Day #_____

Circle your suspected problem foods.
Common allergens: citrus, coffee, corn, dairy, eggs, fish/shellfish, gluten, meat (beef, lamb, pork), peanuts, raw fruits & vegetables, soy, tree nuts

WHAT DID YOU EAT TODAY?

Meal #1, Time/Location _____
_____
_____
_____
_____

Snack #1, Time/Location _____
_____
_____

Meal #2, Time/Location _____
_____
_____
_____
_____

Snack #2, Time/Location _____
_____
_____

Meal #3, Time/Location _____
_____
_____
_____
_____

Snack #3, Time/Location _____
_____
_____

HOW DO YOU FEEL?
(Include Symptom/Time)
_____
_____
_____
_____
_____
_____
_____
_____
_____
_____
_____
_____
_____
_____
_____
_____
_____
_____
_____
_____
_____
_____
_____
_____
_____
_____
_____
_____
_____
_____
_____
_____
_____
_____
_____
_____

EXERCISE: What exercise did you do today? How long? How do you feel?
_____
_____
_____

WATER: Cross off each 8-ounce glass of water you drank today. (Mark other beverages with meals.)

1   2   3   4   5   6   7   8   9   10

LAST NIGHT'S SLEEP

When did you fall asleep last night? _____

When did you wake this morning? _____

How well did you sleep last night? (Rate from 1-10, with 10 being best) _____

Comments about sleep

_____
_____
_____
_____
_____
_____
_____
_____
_____
_____
_____
_____
_____
_____
_____
_____
_____
_____
_____

NEW MEDICATIONS/VITAMINS: List new medications. What side effects did you observe?

_____
_____
_____
_____
_____
_____
_____
_____
_____
_____
_____
_____
_____
_____

VITALS

Blood Sugar/Time _____/_____
Blood Sugar/Time _____/_____

Blood Pressure/Time _____/_____
Blood Pressure/Time _____/_____

Weight _____

BOWEL MOVEMENTS

BM No. 1/Time_____
BM Type (Circle) 1   2   3   4   5   6   7

Observations: _____
_____
_____

BM No. 2/Time_____
BM Type (Circle) 1   2   3   4   5   6   7

Observations: _____
_____
_____

BM No. 3/Time_____
BM Type (Circle) 1   2   3   4   5   6   7

Observations: _____
_____
_____

What challenge did you overcome today?

_____
_____
_____

What are you grateful for?

_____
_____
_____

What's the best thing that happened today?

_____
_____
_____

IT AIN'T JUST THE DIET
FOOD & WELLNESS DAILY LOG

Date: _____ Test Day #_____

Circle your suspected problem foods.
Common allergens: citrus, coffee, corn, dairy, eggs, fish/shellfish, gluten, meat (beef, lamb, pork), peanuts, raw fruits & vegetables, soy, tree nuts

WHAT DID YOU EAT TODAY?

Meal #1, Time/Location _____
_____
_____
_____

Snack #1, Time/Location _____
_____
_____

Meal #2, Time/Location _____
_____
_____
_____

Snack #2, Time/Location _____
_____
_____

Meal #3, Time/Location _____
_____
_____
_____

Snack #3, Time/Location _____
_____

HOW DO YOU FEEL?
(Include Symptom/Time)
_____
_____
_____
_____
_____
_____
_____
_____
_____
_____
_____
_____
_____
_____
_____
_____
_____
_____
_____
_____
_____
_____
_____
_____
_____
_____
_____
_____
_____
_____
_____
_____
_____
_____
_____
_____
_____
_____
_____
_____
_____

EXERCISE: What exercise did you do today? How long? How do you feel?
_____
_____
_____

WATER: Cross off each 8-ounce glass of water you drank today. (Mark other beverages with meals.)

1   2   3   4   5   6   7   8   9   10

LAST NIGHT'S SLEEP

When did you fall asleep last night? _____

When did you wake this morning? _____

How well did you sleep last night? (Rate from 1-10, with 10 being best) _____

Comments about sleep

_____
_____
_____
_____
_____
_____
_____
_____
_____
_____
_____
_____
_____
_____
_____
_____
_____
_____
_____
_____
_____
_____
_____

NEW MEDICATIONS/VITAMINS: List new medications. What side effects did you observe?

_____
_____
_____
_____
_____
_____
_____
_____
_____
_____
_____
_____
_____
_____
_____
_____
_____

VITALS
Blood Sugar/Time _____/_____
Blood Sugar/Time _____/_____

Blood Pressure/Time _____/_____
Blood Pressure/Time _____/_____

Weight _____

BOWEL MOVEMENTS

BM No. 1/Time_____
BM Type (Circle) 1   2   3   4   5   6   7

Observations: _____
_____
_____

BM No. 2/Time_____
BM Type (Circle) 1   2   3   4   5   6   7

Observations: _____
_____
_____

BM No. 3/Time_____
BM Type (Circle) 1   2   3   4   5   6   7

Observations: _____
_____
_____

What challenge did you overcome today?
_____
_____
_____

What are you grateful for?
_____
_____
_____

What's the best thing that happened today?
_____
_____
_____

IT AIN'T JUST THE DIET
FOOD & WELLNESS DAILY LOG

Date: _____ Test Day #_____

Circle your suspected problem foods.
Common allergens: citrus, coffee, corn, dairy, eggs, fish/shellfish, gluten, meat (beef, lamb, pork), peanuts, raw fruits & vegetables, soy, tree nuts

WHAT DID YOU EAT TODAY?

Meal #1, Time/Location _____
_____
_____
_____

Snack #1, Time/Location _____
_____
_____

Meal #2, Time/Location _____
_____
_____
_____

Snack #2, Time/Location _____
_____
_____

Meal #3, Time/Location _____
_____
_____
_____

Snack #3, Time/Location _____
_____
_____

HOW DO YOU FEEL?
(Include Symptom/Time)
_____
_____
_____
_____
_____
_____
_____
_____
_____
_____
_____
_____
_____
_____
_____
_____
_____
_____
_____
_____
_____
_____
_____
_____
_____
_____
_____
_____
_____
_____
_____
_____
_____
_____
_____

EXERCISE: What exercise did you do today? How long? How do you feel?
_____
_____
_____

WATER: Cross off each 8-ounce glass of water you drank today. (Mark other beverages with meals.)

1   2   3   4   5   6   7   8   9   10

LAST NIGHT'S SLEEP

When did you fall asleep last night? _____

When did you wake this morning? _____

How well did you sleep last night? (Rate from 1-10, with 10 being best) _____

Comments about sleep

_____
_____
_____
_____
_____
_____
_____
_____
_____
_____
_____
_____
_____
_____
_____
_____
_____
_____
_____

NEW MEDICATIONS/VITAMINS: List new medications. What side effects did you observe?

_____
_____
_____
_____
_____
_____
_____
_____
_____
_____
_____
_____
_____
_____
_____

VITALS

Blood Sugar/Time _____/_____
Blood Sugar/Time _____/_____

Blood Pressure/Time _____/_____
Blood Pressure/Time _____/_____

Weight _____

BOWEL MOVEMENTS

BM No. 1/Time_____
BM Type (Circle) 1   2   3   4   5   6   7

Observations: _____
_____
_____

BM No. 2/Time_____
BM Type (Circle) 1   2   3   4   5   6   7

Observations: _____
_____
_____

BM No. 3/Time_____
BM Type (Circle) 1   2   3   4   5   6   7

Observations: _____
_____
_____

What challenge did you overcome today?
_____
_____
_____

What are you grateful for?
_____
_____
_____

What's the best thing that happened today?
_____
_____
_____

IT AIN'T JUST THE DIET
FOOD & WELLNESS DAILY LOG

Date: _____ Test Day #_____

Circle your suspected problem foods.
Common allergens: citrus, coffee, corn, dairy, eggs, fish/shellfish, gluten, meat (beef, lamb, pork), peanuts, raw fruits & vegetables, soy, tree nuts

WHAT DID YOU EAT TODAY?

Meal #1, Time/Location _____
_____
_____
_____

Snack #1, Time/Location _____
_____
_____

Meal #2, Time/Location _____
_____
_____
_____

Snack #2, Time/Location _____
_____
_____

Meal #3, Time/Location _____
_____
_____
_____

Snack #3, Time/Location _____
_____
_____

HOW DO YOU FEEL?
(Include Symptom/Time)
_____
_____
_____
_____
_____
_____
_____
_____
_____
_____
_____
_____
_____
_____
_____
_____
_____
_____
_____
_____
_____
_____
_____
_____
_____
_____
_____
_____
_____
_____
_____
_____
_____
_____
_____

EXERCISE: What exercise did you do today? How long? How do you feel?
_____
_____
_____

WATER: Cross off each 8-ounce glass of water you drank today. (Mark other beverages with meals.)

1   2   3   4   5   6   7   8   9   10

LAST NIGHT'S SLEEP

When did you fall asleep last night? _____

When did you wake this morning? _____

How well did you sleep last night? (Rate from 1-10, with 10 being best) _____

Comments about sleep

_____
_____
_____
_____
_____
_____
_____
_____
_____
_____
_____
_____
_____
_____
_____
_____

NEW MEDICATIONS/VITAMINS: List new medications. What side effects did you observe?

_____
_____
_____
_____
_____
_____
_____
_____
_____
_____
_____
_____
_____
_____

VITALS

Blood Sugar/Time _____/_____
Blood Sugar/Time _____/_____

Blood Pressure/Time _____/_____
Blood Pressure/Time _____/_____

Weight _____

BOWEL MOVEMENTS

BM No. 1/Time_____
BM Type (Circle) 1   2   3   4   5   6   7

Observations: _____
_____
_____

BM No. 2/Time_____
BM Type (Circle) 1   2   3   4   5   6   7

Observations: _____
_____
_____

BM No. 3/Time_____
BM Type (Circle) 1   2   3   4   5   6   7

Observations: _____
_____
_____

What challenge did you overcome today?

_____
_____
_____

What are you grateful for?

_____
_____
_____

What's the best thing that happened today?

_____
_____
_____

IT AIN'T JUST THE DIET
FOOD & WELLNESS DAILY LOG

Date: _____ Test Day #_____

Circle your suspected problem foods.
Common allergens: citrus, coffee, corn, dairy, eggs, fish/shellfish, gluten, meat (beef, lamb, pork), peanuts, raw fruits & vegetables, soy, tree nuts

WHAT DID YOU EAT TODAY?

Meal #1, Time/Location _____
_____
_____
_____

Snack #1, Time/Location _____
_____
_____

Meal #2, Time/Location _____
_____
_____
_____

Snack #2, Time/Location _____
_____
_____

Meal #3, Time/Location _____
_____
_____
_____

Snack #3, Time/Location _____
_____
_____

HOW DO YOU FEEL?
(Include Symptom/Time)
_____
_____
_____
_____
_____
_____
_____
_____
_____
_____
_____
_____
_____
_____
_____
_____
_____
_____
_____
_____
_____
_____
_____
_____
_____
_____
_____
_____
_____
_____
_____
_____
_____
_____

EXERCISE: What exercise did you do today? How long? How do you feel?
_____
_____
_____

WATER: Cross off each 8-ounce glass of water you drank today. (Mark other beverages with meals.)

1   2   3   4   5   6   7   8   9   10

LAST NIGHT'S SLEEP

When did you fall asleep last night? _____

When did you wake this morning? _____

How well did you sleep last night? (Rate from 1-10, with 10 being best) _____

Comments about sleep

_____
_____
_____
_____
_____
_____
_____
_____
_____
_____
_____
_____
_____
_____
_____
_____
_____
_____
_____

NEW MEDICATIONS/VITAMINS: List new medications. What side effects did you observe?

_____
_____
_____
_____
_____
_____
_____
_____
_____
_____
_____
_____
_____
_____
_____

VITALS

Blood Sugar/Time _____/_____
Blood Sugar/Time _____/_____

Blood Pressure/Time _____/_____
Blood Pressure/Time _____/_____

Weight _____

BOWEL MOVEMENTS

BM No. 1/Time_____
BM Type (Circle) 1   2   3   4   5   6   7

Observations: _____
_____
_____

BM No. 2/Time_____
BM Type (Circle) 1   2   3   4   5   6   7

Observations: _____
_____
_____

BM No. 3/Time_____
BM Type (Circle) 1   2   3   4   5   6   7

Observations: _____
_____
_____

What challenge did you overcome today?
_____
_____
_____

What are you grateful for?
_____
_____
_____

What's the best thing that happened today?
_____
_____
_____

Food Allergies, Sensitivities, & Intolerances Symptoms Checklist

Week 6 Assessment

Date: _____

Check each symptom you have experienced after eating (currently or in the recent past).

Breathing
- ☐ Sneezing
- ☐ Stuffy nose/sinuses
- ☐ Congestion
- ☐ Runny nose
- ☐ Face pain
- ☐ Difficulty breathing
- ☐ Wheezing or asthma

Skin
- ☐ Hives
- ☐ Eczema or rash
- ☐ Dandruff
- ☐ Ticklishness
- ☐ Flushing
- ☐ Rosy cheeks or ears

Eyes
- ☐ Itchy eyes
- ☐ Dry eyes

Digestive
- ☐ Bloating
- ☐ Gas
- ☐ Constipated
- ☐ Diarrhea or loose stools
- ☐ More bowel movements
- ☐ Fewer bowel movements
- ☐ Abdominal cramping
- ☐ Stinky bowel movements
- ☐ Undigested food in stool
- ☐ Bloody stool

Brain/Thinking
- ☐ Brain fog
- ☐ Inability to concentrate
- ☐ Disjointed or distractible thinking
- ☐ Headaches
- ☐ Glassy-eyed or spacey
- ☐ Trouble remembering things

Energy
- ☐ Hyperactivity
- ☐ Restlessness
- ☐ Tiredness/fatigue
- ☐ Low energy/activity

Difference in Sleep
- ☐ Better
- ☐ Worse
- ☐ Restless leg while sleeping
- ☐ Ideas why? _____

Pain
- ☐ Joint pain
- ☐ Muscle pain
- ☐ Other pain: _____

Mood
- ☐ Ecstatic
- ☐ Happy
- ☐ Neutral
- ☐ Sad
- ☐ Angry/Irritable
- ☐ Calm
- ☐ Anxious
- ☐ Feeling stressed (hair on fire)
- ☐ Filled with creativity
- ☐ Exhausted/no energy

Hunger Changes
- ☐ Craving certain foods (list) _____
- ☐ Hungry all the time
- ☐ Little or no interest in food

Other
- ☐ Bad breath
- ☐ Stinky feet
- ☐ Sweating hands/feet
- ☐ Other: _____

Notes:
_____
_____
_____
_____
_____
_____
_____
_____
_____
_____
_____

Week 6 Journal Prompt

Who supports your food decisions? Write why you appreciate this person.

_____
_____
_____
_____
_____
_____
_____
_____
_____
_____
_____
_____
_____
_____
_____
_____
_____
_____
_____
_____
_____
_____
_____
_____
_____
_____
_____
_____
_____
_____
_____
_____
_____

IT AIN'T JUST THE DIET
FOOD & WELLNESS DAILY LOG

Date: _____ Test Day #_____

Circle your suspected problem foods.
Common allergens: citrus, coffee, corn, dairy, eggs, fish/shellfish, gluten, meat (beef, lamb, pork), peanuts, raw fruits & vegetables, soy, tree nuts

WHAT DID YOU EAT TODAY?

Meal #1, Time/Location _____
_____
_____
_____

Snack #1, Time/Location _____
_____
_____

Meal #2, Time/Location _____
_____
_____
_____

Snack #2, Time/Location _____
_____

Meal #3, Time/Location _____
_____
_____
_____

Snack #3, Time/Location _____
_____
_____

HOW DO YOU FEEL?
(Include Symptom/Time)
_____
_____
_____
_____
_____
_____
_____
_____
_____
_____
_____
_____
_____
_____
_____
_____
_____
_____
_____
_____
_____
_____
_____
_____
_____
_____
_____
_____
_____
_____
_____
_____
_____

EXERCISE: What exercise did you do today? How long? How do you feel?
_____
_____
_____

WATER: Cross off each 8-ounce glass of water you drank today. (Mark other beverages with meals.)

1   2   3   4   5   6   7   8   9   10

LAST NIGHT'S SLEEP

When did you fall asleep last night? _____

When did you wake this morning? _____

How well did you sleep last night? (Rate from 1-10, with 10 being best) _____

Comments about sleep

_____
_____
_____
_____
_____
_____
_____
_____
_____
_____
_____
_____
_____
_____
_____
_____
_____
_____

NEW MEDICATIONS/VITAMINS: List new medications. What side effects did you observe?

_____
_____
_____
_____
_____
_____
_____
_____
_____
_____
_____
_____
_____
_____
_____

VITALS

Blood Sugar/Time _____/_____
Blood Sugar/Time _____/_____

Blood Pressure/Time _____/_____
Blood Pressure/Time _____/_____

Weight _____

BOWEL MOVEMENTS

BM No. 1/Time_____
BM Type (Circle) 1   2   3   4   5   6   7

Observations: _____
_____
_____

BM No. 2/Time_____
BM Type (Circle) 1   2   3   4   5   6   7

Observations: _____
_____
_____

BM No. 3/Time_____
BM Type (Circle) 1   2   3   4   5   6   7

Observations: _____
_____
_____

What challenge did you overcome today?
_____
_____
_____

What are you grateful for?
_____
_____
_____

What's the best thing that happened today?
_____
_____
_____

IT AIN'T JUST THE DIET
FOOD & WELLNESS DAILY LOG

Date: _____ Test Day #_____

Circle your suspected problem foods.
Common allergens: citrus, coffee, corn, dairy,
eggs, fish/shellfish, gluten, meat (beef, lamb,
pork), peanuts, raw fruits & vegetables, soy,
tree nuts

WHAT DID YOU EAT TODAY?

Meal #1, Time/Location _____
_____
_____
_____
_____

Snack #1, Time/Location _____
_____
_____

Meal #2, Time/Location _____
_____
_____
_____
_____

Snack #2, Time/Location _____
_____
_____

Meal #3, Time/Location _____
_____
_____
_____
_____

Snack #3, Time/Location _____
_____
_____

HOW DO YOU FEEL?
(Include Symptom/Time)
_____
_____
_____
_____
_____
_____
_____
_____
_____
_____
_____
_____
_____
_____
_____
_____
_____
_____
_____
_____
_____
_____
_____
_____
_____
_____
_____
_____
_____
_____
_____
_____
_____

EXERCISE: What exercise did you do today?
How long? How do you feel?
_____
_____
_____

WATER: Cross off each 8-ounce glass of water
you drank today. (Mark other beverages with
meals.)

1   2   3   4   5   6   7   8   9   10

LAST NIGHT'S SLEEP

When did you fall asleep last night? _____

When did you wake this morning? _____

How well did you sleep last night? (Rate from 1-10, with 10 being best) _____

Comments about sleep

_____
_____
_____
_____
_____
_____
_____
_____
_____
_____
_____
_____
_____
_____
_____
_____
_____
_____

NEW MEDICATIONS/VITAMINS: List new medications. What side effects did you observe?

_____
_____
_____
_____
_____
_____
_____
_____
_____
_____
_____
_____
_____
_____

VITALS

Blood Sugar/Time _____/_____
Blood Sugar/Time _____/_____

Blood Pressure/Time _____/_____
Blood Pressure/Time _____/_____

Weight _____

BOWEL MOVEMENTS

BM No. 1/Time_____
BM Type (Circle) 1   2   3   4   5   6   7

Observations: _____
_____
_____

BM No. 2/Time_____
BM Type (Circle) 1   2   3   4   5   6   7

Observations: _____
_____
_____

BM No. 3/Time_____
BM Type (Circle) 1   2   3   4   5   6   7

Observations: _____
_____
_____

What challenge did you overcome today?
_____
_____
_____

What are you grateful for?
_____
_____
_____

What's the best thing that happened today?
_____
_____
_____

IT AIN'T JUST THE DIET
FOOD & WELLNESS DAILY LOG

Date: _____ Test Day #_____

Circle your suspected problem foods.
Common allergens: citrus, coffee, corn, dairy, eggs, fish/shellfish, gluten, meat (beef, lamb, pork), peanuts, raw fruits & vegetables, soy, tree nuts

WHAT DID YOU EAT TODAY?

Meal #1, Time/Location _____
_____
_____
_____

Snack #1, Time/Location _____
_____
_____

Meal #2, Time/Location _____
_____
_____
_____

Snack #2, Time/Location _____
_____
_____

Meal #3, Time/Location _____
_____
_____
_____

Snack #3, Time/Location _____
_____
_____

HOW DO YOU FEEL?
(Include Symptom/Time)
_____
_____
_____
_____
_____
_____
_____
_____
_____
_____
_____
_____
_____
_____
_____
_____
_____
_____
_____
_____
_____
_____
_____
_____
_____
_____
_____
_____
_____
_____
_____
_____
_____
_____
_____
_____

EXERCISE: What exercise did you do today? How long? How do you feel?
_____
_____
_____

WATER: Cross off each 8-ounce glass of water you drank today. (Mark other beverages with meals.)

1   2   3   4   5   6   7   8   9   10

LAST NIGHT'S SLEEP

When did you fall asleep last night? _____

When did you wake this morning? _____

How well did you sleep last night? (Rate from 1-10, with 10 being best) _____

Comments about sleep

_____
_____
_____
_____
_____
_____
_____
_____
_____
_____
_____
_____
_____
_____
_____
_____
_____
_____

NEW MEDICATIONS/VITAMINS: List new medications. What side effects did you observe?

_____
_____
_____
_____
_____
_____
_____
_____
_____
_____
_____
_____
_____
_____
_____
_____

VITALS
Blood Sugar/Time _____/_____
Blood Sugar/Time _____/_____

Blood Pressure/Time _____/_____
Blood Pressure/Time _____/_____

Weight _____

BOWEL MOVEMENTS

BM No. 1/Time_____
BM Type (Circle) 1   2   3   4   5   6   7

Observations: _____
_____
_____

BM No. 2/Time_____
BM Type (Circle) 1   2   3   4   5   6   7

Observations: _____
_____
_____

BM No. 3/Time_____
BM Type (Circle) 1   2   3   4   5   6   7

Observations: _____
_____
_____

What challenge did you overcome today?
_____
_____
_____

What are you grateful for?
_____
_____
_____

What's the best thing that happened today?
_____
_____
_____

IT AIN'T JUST THE DIET
FOOD & WELLNESS DAILY LOG

Date: _____ Test Day #_____

Circle your suspected problem foods.
Common allergens: citrus, coffee, corn, dairy, eggs, fish/shellfish, gluten, meat (beef, lamb, pork), peanuts, raw fruits & vegetables, soy, tree nuts

WHAT DID YOU EAT TODAY?

Meal #1, Time/Location _____
_____
_____
_____

Snack #1, Time/Location _____
_____

Meal #2, Time/Location _____
_____
_____
_____

Snack #2, Time/Location _____
_____

Meal #3, Time/Location _____
_____
_____
_____

Snack #3, Time/Location _____
_____

HOW DO YOU FEEL?
(Include Symptom/Time)
_____
_____
_____
_____
_____
_____
_____
_____
_____
_____
_____
_____
_____
_____
_____
_____
_____
_____
_____
_____
_____
_____
_____
_____
_____
_____
_____
_____
_____
_____
_____
_____
_____
_____

EXERCISE: What exercise did you do today? How long? How do you feel?
_____
_____
_____

WATER: Cross off each 8-ounce glass of water you drank today. (Mark other beverages with meals.)

1   2   3   4   5   6   7   8   9   10

LAST NIGHT'S SLEEP

When did you fall asleep last night? _____

When did you wake this morning? _____

How well did you sleep last night? (Rate from 1-10, with 10 being best) _____

Comments about sleep

_____
_____
_____
_____
_____
_____
_____
_____
_____
_____
_____
_____
_____
_____
_____
_____
_____
_____
_____

NEW MEDICATIONS/VITAMINS: List new medications. What side effects did you observe?

_____
_____
_____
_____
_____
_____
_____
_____
_____
_____
_____
_____
_____
_____

VITALS

Blood Sugar/Time _____/_____
Blood Sugar/Time _____/_____

Blood Pressure/Time _____/_____
Blood Pressure/Time _____/_____

Weight _____

BOWEL MOVEMENTS

BM No. 1/Time_____
BM Type (Circle) 1   2   3   4   5   6   7

Observations: _____
_____
_____

BM No. 2/Time_____
BM Type (Circle) 1   2   3   4   5   6   7

Observations: _____
_____
_____

BM No. 3/Time_____
BM Type (Circle) 1   2   3   4   5   6   7

Observations: _____
_____
_____

What challenge did you overcome today?

_____
_____
_____

What are you grateful for?

_____
_____
_____

What's the best thing that happened today?

_____
_____
_____

IT AIN'T JUST THE DIET
FOOD & WELLNESS DAILY LOG

Date: _____ Test Day #_____

Circle your suspected problem foods.
Common allergens: citrus, coffee, corn, dairy, eggs, fish/shellfish, gluten, meat (beef, lamb, pork), peanuts, raw fruits & vegetables, soy, tree nuts

WHAT DID YOU EAT TODAY?

Meal #1, Time/Location _____
_____
_____
_____

Snack #1, Time/Location _____
_____

Meal #2, Time/Location _____
_____
_____
_____

Snack #2, Time/Location _____
_____

Meal #3, Time/Location _____
_____
_____
_____

Snack #3, Time/Location _____
_____
_____

HOW DO YOU FEEL?
(Include Symptom/Time)
_____
_____
_____
_____
_____
_____
_____
_____
_____
_____
_____
_____
_____
_____
_____
_____
_____
_____
_____
_____
_____
_____
_____
_____
_____
_____
_____
_____
_____
_____
_____
_____

EXERCISE: What exercise did you do today? How long? How do you feel?
_____
_____
_____

WATER: Cross off each 8-ounce glass of water you drank today. (Mark other beverages with meals.)

1   2   3   4   5   6   7   8   9   10

LAST NIGHT'S SLEEP

When did you fall asleep last night? _____

When did you wake this morning? _____

How well did you sleep last night? (Rate from 1-10, with 10 being best) _____

Comments about sleep

_____
_____
_____
_____
_____
_____
_____
_____
_____
_____
_____
_____
_____
_____
_____
_____
_____
_____
_____
_____

NEW MEDICATIONS/VITAMINS: List new medications. What side effects did you observe?

_____
_____
_____
_____
_____
_____
_____
_____
_____
_____
_____
_____
_____
_____
_____
_____

VITALS

Blood Sugar/Time _____/_____
Blood Sugar/Time _____/_____

Blood Pressure/Time _____/_____
Blood Pressure/Time _____/_____

Weight _____

BOWEL MOVEMENTS

BM No. 1/Time_____
BM Type (Circle) 1   2   3   4   5   6   7

Observations: _____
_____
_____

BM No. 2/Time_____
BM Type (Circle) 1   2   3   4   5   6   7

Observations: _____
_____
_____

BM No. 3/Time_____
BM Type (Circle) 1   2   3   4   5   6   7

Observations: _____
_____
_____

What challenge did you overcome today?
_____
_____
_____
_____

What are you grateful for?
_____
_____
_____

What's the best thing that happened today?
_____
_____
_____
_____

IT AIN'T JUST THE DIET
FOOD & WELLNESS DAILY LOG

Date: _____ Test Day #_____

Circle your suspected problem foods.
Common allergens: citrus, coffee, corn, dairy, eggs, fish/shellfish, gluten, meat (beef, lamb, pork), peanuts, raw fruits & vegetables, soy, tree nuts

WHAT DID YOU EAT TODAY?

Meal #1, Time/Location _____
_____
_____
_____

Snack #1, Time/Location _____
_____
_____

Meal #2, Time/Location _____
_____
_____
_____

Snack #2, Time/Location _____
_____
_____

Meal #3, Time/Location _____
_____
_____
_____

Snack #3, Time/Location _____
_____
_____

HOW DO YOU FEEL?
(Include Symptom/Time)
_____
_____
_____
_____
_____
_____
_____
_____
_____
_____
_____
_____
_____
_____
_____
_____
_____
_____
_____
_____
_____
_____
_____
_____
_____
_____
_____
_____
_____
_____
_____
_____
_____
_____
_____
_____

EXERCISE: What exercise did you do today? How long? How do you feel?
_____
_____
_____

WATER: Cross off each 8-ounce glass of water you drank today. (Mark other beverages with meals.)

1   2   3   4   5   6   7   8   9   10

LAST NIGHT'S SLEEP

When did you fall asleep last night? _____

When did you wake this morning? _____

How well did you sleep last night? (Rate from 1-10, with 10 being best) _____

Comments about sleep

_____
_____
_____
_____
_____
_____
_____
_____
_____
_____
_____
_____
_____
_____
_____
_____
_____

NEW MEDICATIONS/VITAMINS: List new medications. What side effects did you observe?

_____
_____
_____
_____
_____
_____
_____
_____
_____
_____
_____
_____
_____
_____

VITALS

Blood Sugar/Time _____/_____
Blood Sugar/Time _____/_____

Blood Pressure/Time _____/_____
Blood Pressure/Time _____/_____

Weight _____

BOWEL MOVEMENTS

BM No. 1/Time_____
BM Type (Circle) 1   2   3   4   5   6   7

Observations: _____
_____
_____

BM No. 2/Time_____
BM Type (Circle) 1   2   3   4   5   6   7

Observations: _____
_____
_____

BM No. 3/Time_____
BM Type (Circle) 1   2   3   4   5   6   7

Observations: _____
_____
_____

What challenge did you overcome today?

_____
_____
_____

What are you grateful for?

_____
_____
_____

What's the best thing that happened today?

_____
_____
_____

IT AIN'T JUST THE DIET
FOOD & WELLNESS DAILY LOG

Date: _____ Test Day #_____

Circle your suspected problem foods.
Common allergens: citrus, coffee, corn, dairy, eggs, fish/shellfish, gluten, meat (beef, lamb, pork), peanuts, raw fruits & vegetables, soy, tree nuts

WHAT DID YOU EAT TODAY?

Meal #1, Time/Location _____
_____
_____
_____

Snack #1, Time/Location _____
_____
_____

Meal #2, Time/Location _____
_____
_____
_____

Snack #2, Time/Location _____
_____
_____

Meal #3, Time/Location _____
_____
_____
_____

Snack #3, Time/Location _____
_____
_____

EXERCISE: What exercise did you do today? How long? How do you feel?
_____
_____
_____

HOW DO YOU FEEL?
(Include Symptom/Time)

_____
_____
_____
_____
_____
_____
_____
_____
_____
_____
_____
_____
_____
_____
_____
_____
_____
_____
_____
_____
_____
_____
_____
_____
_____
_____
_____
_____
_____
_____
_____
_____
_____
_____
_____
_____

WATER: Cross off each 8-ounce glass of water you drank today. (Mark other beverages with meals.)

1   2   3   4   5   6   7   8   9   10

LAST NIGHT'S SLEEP

When did you fall asleep last night? _____

When did you wake this morning? _____

How well did you sleep last night? (Rate from 1-10, with 10 being best) _____

Comments about sleep

_____
_____
_____
_____
_____
_____
_____
_____
_____
_____
_____
_____
_____
_____
_____
_____
_____
_____

NEW MEDICATIONS/VITAMINS: List new medications. What side effects did you observe?

_____
_____
_____
_____
_____
_____
_____
_____
_____
_____
_____
_____
_____
_____
_____

VITALS
Blood Sugar/Time _____/_____
Blood Sugar/Time _____/_____

Blood Pressure/Time _____/_____
Blood Pressure/Time _____/_____

Weight _____

BOWEL MOVEMENTS

BM No. 1/Time_____
BM Type (Circle) 1   2   3   4   5   6   7

Observations: _____
_____
_____

BM No. 2/Time_____
BM Type (Circle) 1   2   3   4   5   6   7

Observations: _____
_____
_____

BM No. 3/Time_____
BM Type (Circle) 1   2   3   4   5   6   7

Observations: _____
_____
_____

What challenge did you overcome today?
_____
_____
_____

What are you grateful for?
_____
_____
_____

What's the best thing that happened today?
_____
_____
_____

Food Allergies, Sensitivities, & Intolerances Symptoms Checklist

Week 7 Assessment

Date: _____

Check each symptom you have experienced after eating (currently or in the recent past).

Breathing
- ☐ Sneezing
- ☐ Stuffy nose/sinuses
- ☐ Congestion
- ☐ Runny nose
- ☐ Face pain
- ☐ Difficulty breathing
- ☐ Wheezing or asthma

Skin
- ☐ Hives
- ☐ Eczema or rash
- ☐ Dandruff
- ☐ Ticklishness
- ☐ Flushing
- ☐ Rosy cheeks or ears

Eyes
- ☐ Itchy eyes
- ☐ Dry eyes

Digestive
- ☐ Bloating
- ☐ Gas
- ☐ Constipated
- ☐ Diarrhea or loose stools
- ☐ More bowel movements
- ☐ Fewer bowel movements
- ☐ Abdominal cramping
- ☐ Stinky bowel movements
- ☐ Undigested food in stool
- ☐ Bloody stool

Brain/Thinking
- ☐ Brain fog
- ☐ Inability to concentrate
- ☐ Disjointed or distractible thinking
- ☐ Headaches
- ☐ Glassy-eyed or spacey
- ☐ Trouble remembering things

Energy
- ☐ Hyperactivity
- ☐ Restlessness
- ☐ Tiredness/fatigue
- ☐ Low energy/activity

Difference in Sleep
- ☐ Better
- ☐ Worse
- ☐ Restless leg while sleeping
- ☐ Ideas why? _____

Pain
- ☐ Joint pain
- ☐ Muscle pain
- ☐ Other pain: _____

Mood
- ☐ Ecstatic
- ☐ Happy
- ☐ Neutral
- ☐ Sad
- ☐ Angry/Irritable
- ☐ Calm
- ☐ Anxious
- ☐ Feeling stressed (hair on fire)
- ☐ Filled with creativity
- ☐ Exhausted/no energy

Hunger Changes
- ☐ Craving certain foods (list) _____
- ☐ Hungry all the time
- ☐ Little or no interest in food

Other
- ☐ Bad breath
- ☐ Stinky feet
- ☐ Sweating hands/feet
- ☐ Other: _____

Notes:
_____
_____
_____
_____
_____
_____
_____
_____
_____
_____
_____

Week 7 Journal Prompt

What was the most surprising discovery you made last week? How will that affect what you do next week?

_____

_____

_____

_____

_____

_____

_____

_____

_____

_____

_____

_____

_____

_____

_____

_____

_____

_____

_____

_____

_____

_____

_____

_____

_____

_____

_____

_____

_____

_____

IT AIN'T JUST THE DIET
FOOD & WELLNESS DAILY LOG

Date: _____ Test Day # _____

Circle your suspected problem foods.
Common allergens: citrus, coffee, corn, dairy, eggs, fish/shellfish, gluten, meat (beef, lamb, pork), peanuts, raw fruits & vegetables, soy, tree nuts

WHAT DID YOU EAT TODAY?

Meal #1, Time/Location _____
_____
_____
_____

Snack #1, Time/Location _____
_____
_____

Meal #2, Time/Location _____
_____
_____
_____

Snack #2, Time/Location _____
_____
_____

Meal #3, Time/Location _____
_____
_____
_____

Snack #3, Time/Location _____
_____
_____

HOW DO YOU FEEL?
(Include Symptom/Time)
_____
_____
_____
_____
_____
_____
_____
_____
_____
_____
_____
_____
_____
_____
_____
_____
_____
_____
_____
_____
_____
_____
_____
_____
_____
_____
_____
_____
_____
_____
_____
_____
_____
_____

EXERCISE: What exercise did you do today? How long? How do you feel?
_____
_____
_____

WATER: Cross off each 8-ounce glass of water you drank today. (Mark other beverages with meals.)

1   2   3   4   5   6   7   8   9   10

LAST NIGHT'S SLEEP

When did you fall asleep last night? _____

When did you wake this morning? _____

How well did you sleep last night? (Rate from 1-10, with 10 being best) _____

Comments about sleep

_____
_____
_____
_____
_____
_____
_____
_____
_____
_____
_____
_____
_____
_____
_____
_____
_____
_____
_____

NEW MEDICATIONS/VITAMINS: List new medications. What side effects did you observe?

_____
_____
_____
_____
_____
_____
_____
_____
_____
_____
_____
_____
_____

VITALS

Blood Sugar/Time _____/_____
Blood Sugar/Time _____/_____

Blood Pressure/Time _____/_____
Blood Pressure/Time _____/_____

Weight _____

BOWEL MOVEMENTS

BM No. 1/Time_____
BM Type (Circle) 1   2   3   4   5   6   7

Observations: _____
_____
_____

BM No. 2/Time_____
BM Type (Circle) 1   2   3   4   5   6   7

Observations: _____
_____
_____

BM No. 3/Time_____
BM Type (Circle) 1   2   3   4   5   6   7

Observations: _____
_____
_____

What challenge did you overcome today?

_____
_____
_____

What are you grateful for?

_____
_____
_____

What's the best thing that happened today?

_____
_____
_____

IT AIN'T JUST THE DIET
FOOD & WELLNESS DAILY LOG

Date: _____ Test Day #_____

Circle your suspected problem foods.
Common allergens: citrus, coffee, corn, dairy, eggs, fish/shellfish, gluten, meat (beef, lamb, pork), peanuts, raw fruits & vegetables, soy, tree nuts

WHAT DID YOU EAT TODAY?

Meal #1, Time/Location _____
_____
_____
_____

Snack #1, Time/Location _____
_____
_____

Meal #2, Time/Location _____
_____
_____
_____

Snack #2, Time/Location _____
_____
_____

Meal #3, Time/Location _____
_____
_____
_____

Snack #3, Time/Location _____
_____
_____

HOW DO YOU FEEL?
(Include Symptom/Time)
_____
_____
_____
_____
_____
_____
_____
_____
_____
_____
_____
_____
_____
_____
_____
_____
_____
_____
_____
_____
_____
_____
_____
_____
_____
_____
_____
_____
_____
_____
_____
_____
_____
_____

EXERCISE: What exercise did you do today? How long? How do you feel?
_____
_____
_____

WATER: Cross off each 8-ounce glass of water you drank today. (Mark other beverages with meals.)

1   2   3   4   5   6   7   8   9   10

LAST NIGHT'S SLEEP

When did you fall asleep last night? _____

When did you wake this morning? _____

How well did you sleep last night? (Rate from
1-10, with 10 being best) _____

Comments about sleep

_____
_____
_____
_____
_____
_____
_____
_____
_____
_____
_____
_____
_____
_____
_____
_____
_____

NEW MEDICATIONS/VITAMINS: List new
medications. What side effects did you
observe?

_____
_____
_____
_____
_____
_____
_____
_____
_____
_____
_____
_____
_____
_____
_____

VITALS

Blood Sugar/Time _____/_____
Blood Sugar/Time _____/_____

Blood Pressure/Time _____/_____
Blood Pressure/Time _____/_____

Weight _____

BOWEL MOVEMENTS

BM No. 1/Time_____
BM Type (Circle) 1   2   3   4   5   6   7

Observations: _____
_____
_____

BM No. 2/Time_____
BM Type (Circle) 1   2   3   4   5   6   7

Observations: _____
_____
_____

BM No. 3/Time_____
BM Type (Circle) 1   2   3   4   5   6   7

Observations: _____
_____
_____

What challenge did you overcome today?
_____
_____
_____

What are you grateful for?
_____
_____
_____

What's the best thing that happened today?
_____
_____
_____

IT AIN'T JUST THE DIET
FOOD & WELLNESS DAILY LOG

Date: _____ Test Day #_____

Circle your suspected problem foods.
Common allergens: citrus, coffee, corn, dairy,
eggs, fish/shellfish, gluten, meat (beef, lamb,
pork), peanuts, raw fruits & vegetables, soy,
tree nuts

WHAT DID YOU EAT TODAY?

Meal #1, Time/Location _____
_____
_____
_____
_____

Snack #1, Time/Location _____
_____
_____

Meal #2, Time/Location _____
_____
_____
_____
_____

Snack #2, Time/Location _____
_____
_____

Meal #3, Time/Location _____
_____
_____
_____
_____

Snack #3, Time/Location _____
_____
_____

EXERCISE: What exercise did you do today?
How long? How do you feel?
_____
_____
_____

HOW DO YOU FEEL?
(Include Symptom/Time)
_____
_____
_____
_____
_____
_____
_____
_____
_____
_____
_____
_____
_____
_____
_____
_____
_____
_____
_____
_____
_____
_____
_____
_____
_____
_____
_____
_____
_____
_____
_____
_____
_____
_____
_____
_____
_____

WATER: Cross off each 8-ounce glass of water
you drank today. (Mark other beverages with
meals.)

1   2   3   4   5   6   7   8   9   10

LAST NIGHT'S SLEEP

When did you fall asleep last night? _____

When did you wake this morning? _____

How well did you sleep last night? (Rate from
1-10, with 10 being best) _____

Comments about sleep

_____
_____
_____
_____
_____
_____
_____
_____
_____
_____
_____
_____
_____
_____
_____
_____
_____
_____
_____

NEW MEDICATIONS/VITAMINS: List new
medications. What side effects did you
observe?

_____
_____
_____
_____
_____
_____
_____
_____
_____
_____
_____
_____
_____
_____
_____

VITALS
Blood Sugar/Time _____/_____
Blood Sugar/Time _____/_____

Blood Pressure/Time _____/_____
Blood Pressure/Time _____/_____

Weight _____

BOWEL MOVEMENTS

BM No. 1/Time_____
BM Type (Circle) 1   2   3   4   5   6   7

Observations: _____
_____
_____

BM No. 2/Time_____
BM Type (Circle) 1   2   3   4   5   6   7

Observations: _____
_____
_____

BM No. 3/Time_____
BM Type (Circle) 1   2   3   4   5   6   7

Observations: _____
_____
_____

What challenge did you overcome today?
_____
_____
_____

What are you grateful for?
_____
_____
_____

What's the best thing that happened today?
_____
_____
_____

IT AIN'T JUST THE DIET
FOOD & WELLNESS DAILY LOG

Date: _____ Test Day #_____

Circle your suspected problem foods.
Common allergens: citrus, coffee, corn, dairy, eggs, fish/shellfish, gluten, meat (beef, lamb, pork), peanuts, raw fruits & vegetables, soy, tree nuts

WHAT DID YOU EAT TODAY?

Meal #1, Time/Location _____
_____
_____
_____

Snack #1, Time/Location _____
_____
_____

Meal #2, Time/Location _____
_____
_____
_____

Snack #2, Time/Location _____
_____
_____

Meal #3, Time/Location _____
_____
_____
_____

Snack #3, Time/Location _____
_____
_____

EXERCISE: What exercise did you do today? How long? How do you feel?
_____
_____
_____

HOW DO YOU FEEL?
(Include Symptom/Time)
_____
_____
_____
_____
_____
_____
_____
_____
_____
_____
_____
_____
_____
_____
_____
_____
_____
_____
_____
_____
_____
_____
_____
_____
_____
_____
_____
_____
_____
_____
_____
_____
_____

WATER: Cross off each 8-ounce glass of water you drank today. (Mark other beverages with meals.)

1   2   3   4   5   6   7   8   9   10

LAST NIGHT'S SLEEP

When did you fall asleep last night? _____

When did you wake this morning? _____

How well did you sleep last night? (Rate from 1-10, with 10 being best) _____

Comments about sleep

_____
_____
_____
_____
_____
_____
_____
_____
_____
_____
_____
_____
_____
_____
_____
_____
_____
_____
_____

NEW MEDICATIONS/VITAMINS: List new medications. What side effects did you observe?

_____
_____
_____
_____
_____
_____
_____
_____
_____
_____
_____
_____
_____
_____

VITALS

Blood Sugar/Time _____/_____
Blood Sugar/Time _____/_____

Blood Pressure/Time _____/_____
Blood Pressure/Time _____/_____

Weight _____

BOWEL MOVEMENTS

BM No. 1/Time_____
BM Type (Circle) 1   2   3   4   5   6   7

Observations: _____
_____
_____

BM No. 2/Time_____
BM Type (Circle) 1   2   3   4   5   6   7

Observations: _____
_____
_____

BM No. 3/Time_____
BM Type (Circle) 1   2   3   4   5   6   7

Observations: _____
_____
_____

What challenge did you overcome today?
_____
_____
_____

What are you grateful for?
_____
_____
_____

What's the best thing that happened today?
_____
_____
_____

IT AIN'T JUST THE DIET
FOOD & WELLNESS DAILY LOG

Date: _____ Test Day #_____

Circle your suspected problem foods.
Common allergens: citrus, coffee, corn, dairy, eggs, fish/shellfish, gluten, meat (beef, lamb, pork), peanuts, raw fruits & vegetables, soy, tree nuts

WHAT DID YOU EAT TODAY?

Meal #1, Time/Location _____
_____
_____
_____

Snack #1, Time/Location _____
_____
_____

Meal #2, Time/Location _____
_____
_____
_____

Snack #2, Time/Location _____
_____
_____

Meal #3, Time/Location _____
_____
_____
_____

Snack #3, Time/Location _____
_____

HOW DO YOU FEEL?
(Include Symptom/Time)
_____
_____
_____
_____
_____
_____
_____
_____
_____
_____
_____
_____
_____
_____
_____
_____
_____
_____
_____
_____
_____
_____
_____
_____
_____
_____
_____
_____
_____
_____
_____
_____
_____
_____
_____
_____

EXERCISE: What exercise did you do today? How long? How do you feel?
_____
_____
_____

WATER: Cross off each 8-ounce glass of water you drank today. (Mark other beverages with meals.)

1   2   3   4   5   6   7   8   9   10

LAST NIGHT'S SLEEP

When did you fall asleep last night? _____

When did you wake this morning? _____

How well did you sleep last night? (Rate from 1-10, with 10 being best) _____

Comments about sleep

_____
_____
_____
_____
_____
_____
_____
_____
_____
_____
_____
_____
_____
_____
_____
_____
_____
_____

NEW MEDICATIONS/VITAMINS: List new medications. What side effects did you observe?

_____
_____
_____
_____
_____
_____
_____
_____
_____
_____
_____
_____
_____

VITALS

Blood Sugar/Time _____/_____
Blood Sugar/Time _____/_____

Blood Pressure/Time _____/_____
Blood Pressure/Time _____/_____

Weight _____

BOWEL MOVEMENTS

BM No. 1/Time_____
BM Type (Circle) 1   2   3   4   5   6   7

Observations: _____
_____
_____

BM No. 2/Time_____
BM Type (Circle) 1   2   3   4   5   6   7

Observations: _____
_____
_____

BM No. 3/Time_____
BM Type (Circle) 1   2   3   4   5   6   7

Observations: _____
_____
_____

What challenge did you overcome today?
_____
_____
_____

What are you grateful for?
_____
_____
_____

What's the best thing that happened today?
_____
_____
_____

IT AIN'T JUST THE DIET
FOOD & WELLNESS DAILY LOG

Date: _____ Test Day # _____

Circle your suspected problem foods.
Common allergens: citrus, coffee, corn, dairy, eggs, fish/shellfish, gluten, meat (beef, lamb, pork), peanuts, raw fruits & vegetables, soy, tree nuts

WHAT DID YOU EAT TODAY?

Meal #1, Time/Location _____

_____

_____

_____

Snack #1, Time/Location _____

_____

Meal #2, Time/Location _____

_____

_____

_____

Snack #2, Time/Location _____

_____

Meal #3, Time/Location _____

_____

_____

_____

Snack #3, Time/Location _____

_____

EXERCISE: What exercise did you do today? How long? How do you feel?

_____

_____

_____

HOW DO YOU FEEL?
(Include Symptom/Time)

_____
_____
_____
_____
_____
_____
_____
_____
_____
_____
_____
_____
_____
_____
_____
_____
_____
_____
_____
_____
_____
_____
_____
_____
_____
_____
_____
_____
_____
_____
_____
_____

WATER: Cross off each 8-ounce glass of water you drank today. (Mark other beverages with meals.)

1   2   3   4   5   6   7   8   9   10

LAST NIGHT'S SLEEP

When did you fall asleep last night? _____

When did you wake this morning? _____

How well did you sleep last night? (Rate from 1-10, with 10 being best) _____

Comments about sleep

_____
_____
_____
_____
_____
_____
_____
_____
_____
_____
_____
_____
_____
_____
_____
_____
_____
_____
_____

NEW MEDICATIONS/VITAMINS: List new medications. What side effects did you observe?

_____
_____
_____
_____
_____
_____
_____
_____
_____
_____
_____
_____
_____
_____
_____

VITALS

Blood Sugar/Time _____/_____
Blood Sugar/Time _____/_____

Blood Pressure/Time _____/_____
Blood Pressure/Time _____/_____

Weight _____

BOWEL MOVEMENTS

BM No. 1/Time_____
BM Type (Circle) 1   2   3   4   5   6   7

Observations: _____
_____
_____

BM No. 2/Time_____
BM Type (Circle) 1   2   3   4   5   6   7

Observations: _____
_____
_____

BM No. 3/Time_____
BM Type (Circle) 1   2   3   4   5   6   7

Observations: _____
_____
_____

What challenge did you overcome today?
_____
_____
_____

What are you grateful for?
_____
_____
_____

What's the best thing that happened today?
_____
_____
_____

IT AIN'T JUST THE DIET
FOOD & WELLNESS DAILY LOG

Date: _____ Test Day #_____

Circle your suspected problem foods.
Common allergens: citrus, coffee, corn, dairy, eggs, fish/shellfish, gluten, meat (beef, lamb, pork), peanuts, raw fruits & vegetables, soy, tree nuts

WHAT DID YOU EAT TODAY?

Meal #1, Time/Location _____
_____
_____
_____

Snack #1, Time/Location _____
_____

Meal #2, Time/Location _____
_____
_____
_____

Snack #2, Time/Location _____
_____

Meal #3, Time/Location _____
_____
_____
_____

Snack #3, Time/Location _____
_____
_____

EXERCISE: What exercise did you do today? How long? How do you feel?
_____
_____
_____

HOW DO YOU FEEL?
(Include Symptom/Time)
_____
_____
_____
_____
_____
_____
_____
_____
_____
_____
_____
_____
_____
_____
_____
_____
_____
_____
_____
_____
_____
_____
_____
_____
_____
_____
_____
_____
_____
_____
_____
_____
_____
_____
_____

WATER: Cross off each 8-ounce glass of water you drank today. (Mark other beverages with meals.)

1   2   3   4   5   6   7   8   9   10

LAST NIGHT'S SLEEP

When did you fall asleep last night? _____

When did you wake this morning? _____

How well did you sleep last night? (Rate from 1-10, with 10 being best) _____

Comments about sleep

_____
_____
_____
_____
_____
_____
_____
_____
_____
_____
_____
_____
_____
_____
_____
_____
_____
_____
_____

NEW MEDICATIONS/VITAMINS: List new medications. What side effects did you observe?

_____
_____
_____
_____
_____
_____
_____
_____
_____
_____
_____
_____
_____
_____

VITALS

Blood Sugar/Time _____/_____
Blood Sugar/Time _____/_____

Blood Pressure/Time _____/_____
Blood Pressure/Time _____/_____

Weight _____

BOWEL MOVEMENTS

BM No. 1/Time_____
BM Type (Circle) 1   2   3   4   5   6   7

Observations: _____
_____
_____

BM No. 2/Time_____
BM Type (Circle) 1   2   3   4   5   6   7

Observations: _____
_____
_____

BM No. 3/Time_____
BM Type (Circle) 1   2   3   4   5   6   7

Observations: _____
_____
_____

What challenge did you overcome today?

_____
_____
_____

What are you grateful for?

_____
_____
_____

What's the best thing that happened today?

_____
_____
_____

Food Allergies, Sensitivities, & Intolerances Symptoms Checklist

Week 8 Assessment

Date: _____

Check each symptom you have experienced after eating (currently or in the recent past).

Breathing
- ☐ Sneezing
- ☐ Stuffy nose/sinuses
- ☐ Congestion
- ☐ Runny nose
- ☐ Face pain
- ☐ Difficulty breathing
- ☐ Wheezing or asthma

Skin
- ☐ Hives
- ☐ Eczema or rash
- ☐ Dandruff
- ☐ Ticklishness
- ☐ Flushing
- ☐ Rosy cheeks or ears

Eyes
- ☐ Itchy eyes
- ☐ Dry eyes

Digestive
- ☐ Bloating
- ☐ Gas
- ☐ Constipated
- ☐ Diarrhea or loose stools
- ☐ More bowel movements
- ☐ Fewer bowel movements
- ☐ Abdominal cramping
- ☐ Stinky bowel movements
- ☐ Undigested food in stool
- ☐ Bloody stool

Brain/Thinking
- ☐ Brain fog
- ☐ Inability to concentrate
- ☐ Disjointed or distractible thinking
- ☐ Headaches
- ☐ Glassy-eyed or spacey
- ☐ Trouble remembering things

Energy
- ☐ Hyperactivity
- ☐ Restlessness
- ☐ Tiredness/fatigue
- ☐ Low energy/activity

Difference in Sleep
- ☐ Better
- ☐ Worse
- ☐ Restless leg while sleeping
- ☐ Ideas why? _____

Pain
- ☐ Joint pain
- ☐ Muscle pain
- ☐ Other pain: _____

Mood
- ☐ Ecstatic
- ☐ Happy
- ☐ Neutral
- ☐ Sad
- ☐ Angry/Irritable
- ☐ Calm
- ☐ Anxious
- ☐ Feeling stressed (hair on fire)
- ☐ Filled with creativity
- ☐ Exhausted/no energy

Hunger Changes
- ☐ Craving certain foods (list) _____
- ☐ Hungry all the time
- ☐ Little or no interest in food

Other
- ☐ Bad breath
- ☐ Stinky feet
- ☐ Sweating hands/feet
- ☐ Other: _____

Notes:

_____
_____
_____
_____
_____
_____
_____
_____
_____
_____
_____

Week 8 Journal Prompt

What challenge did you overcome last week? How did you celebrate the win?

_____
_____
_____
_____
_____
_____
_____
_____
_____
_____
_____
_____
_____
_____
_____
_____
_____
_____
_____
_____
_____
_____
_____
_____
_____
_____
_____
_____
_____
_____
_____

IT AIN'T JUST THE DIET
FOOD & WELLNESS DAILY LOG

Date: _____ Test Day #_____

Circle your suspected problem foods.
Common allergens: citrus, coffee, corn, dairy, eggs, fish/shellfish, gluten, meat (beef, lamb, pork), peanuts, raw fruits & vegetables, soy, tree nuts

WHAT DID YOU EAT TODAY?

Meal #1, Time/Location _____
_____
_____
_____
_____

Snack #1, Time/Location _____
_____
_____

Meal #2, Time/Location _____
_____
_____
_____
_____

Snack #2, Time/Location _____
_____
_____

Meal #3, Time/Location _____
_____
_____
_____
_____

Snack #3, Time/Location _____
_____
_____

HOW DO YOU FEEL?
(Include Symptom/Time)
_____
_____
_____
_____
_____
_____
_____
_____
_____
_____
_____
_____
_____
_____
_____
_____
_____
_____
_____
_____
_____
_____
_____
_____
_____
_____
_____
_____
_____
_____
_____
_____
_____
_____
_____
_____
_____
_____

EXERCISE: What exercise did you do today? How long? How do you feel?
_____
_____
_____

WATER: Cross off each 8-ounce glass of water you drank today. (Mark other beverages with meals.)

1   2   3   4   5   6   7   8   9   10

LAST NIGHT'S SLEEP

When did you fall asleep last night? _____

When did you wake this morning? _____

How well did you sleep last night? (Rate from 1-10, with 10 being best) _____

Comments about sleep

_____
_____
_____
_____
_____
_____
_____
_____
_____
_____
_____
_____
_____
_____
_____
_____
_____
_____
_____
_____

NEW MEDICATIONS/VITAMINS: List new medications. What side effects did you observe?

_____
_____
_____
_____
_____
_____
_____
_____
_____
_____
_____
_____
_____
_____
_____

VITALS

Blood Sugar/Time _____/_____
Blood Sugar/Time _____/_____

Blood Pressure/Time _____/_____
Blood Pressure/Time _____/_____

Weight _____

BOWEL MOVEMENTS

BM No. 1/Time_____
BM Type (Circle) 1   2   3   4   5   6   7

Observations: _____
_____
_____

BM No. 2/Time_____
BM Type (Circle) 1   2   3   4   5   6   7

Observations: _____
_____
_____

BM No. 3/Time_____
BM Type (Circle) 1   2   3   4   5   6   7

Observations: _____
_____
_____

What challenge did you overcome today?
_____
_____
_____

What are you grateful for?
_____
_____
_____

What's the best thing that happened today?
_____
_____
_____

IT AIN'T JUST THE DIET
FOOD & WELLNESS DAILY LOG

Date: _____ Test Day #_____

Circle your suspected problem foods.
Common allergens: citrus, coffee, corn, dairy, eggs, fish/shellfish, gluten, meat (beef, lamb, pork), peanuts, raw fruits & vegetables, soy, tree nuts

WHAT DID YOU EAT TODAY?

Meal #1, Time/Location _____

_____
_____
_____

Snack #1, Time/Location _____

_____
_____

Meal #2, Time/Location _____

_____
_____
_____

Snack #2, Time/Location _____

_____
_____

Meal #3, Time/Location _____

_____
_____
_____

Snack #3, Time/Location _____

_____

HOW DO YOU FEEL?
(Include Symptom/Time)

_____
_____
_____
_____
_____
_____
_____
_____
_____
_____
_____
_____
_____
_____
_____
_____
_____
_____
_____
_____
_____
_____
_____
_____
_____
_____
_____
_____
_____
_____
_____
_____
_____

EXERCISE: What exercise did you do today? How long? How do you feel?

_____
_____
_____

WATER: Cross off each 8-ounce glass of water you drank today. (Mark other beverages with meals.)

1   2   3   4   5   6   7   8   9   10

LAST NIGHT'S SLEEP

When did you fall asleep last night? _____

When did you wake this morning? _____

How well did you sleep last night? (Rate from 1-10, with 10 being best) _____

Comments about sleep

_____
_____
_____
_____
_____
_____
_____
_____
_____
_____
_____
_____
_____
_____
_____
_____
_____
_____

NEW MEDICATIONS/VITAMINS: List new medications. What side effects did you observe?

_____
_____
_____
_____
_____
_____
_____
_____
_____
_____
_____
_____
_____

VITALS

Blood Sugar/Time _____/_____
Blood Sugar/Time _____/_____

Blood Pressure/Time _____/_____
Blood Pressure/Time _____/_____

Weight _____

BOWEL MOVEMENTS

BM No. 1/Time_____
BM Type (Circle) 1   2   3   4   5   6   7

Observations: _____
_____
_____

BM No. 2/Time_____
BM Type (Circle) 1   2   3   4   5   6   7

Observations: _____
_____
_____

BM No. 3/Time_____
BM Type (Circle) 1   2   3   4   5   6   7

Observations: _____
_____
_____

What challenge did you overcome today?

_____
_____
_____

What are you grateful for?

_____
_____
_____

What's the best thing that happened today?

_____
_____
_____

IT AIN'T JUST THE DIET
FOOD & WELLNESS DAILY LOG

Date: _____ Test Day #_____

Circle your suspected problem foods.
Common allergens: citrus, coffee, corn, dairy, eggs, fish/shellfish, gluten, meat (beef, lamb, pork), peanuts, raw fruits & vegetables, soy, tree nuts

WHAT DID YOU EAT TODAY?

Meal #1, Time/Location _____
_____
_____
_____

Snack #1, Time/Location _____
_____
_____

Meal #2, Time/Location _____
_____
_____
_____

Snack #2, Time/Location _____
_____
_____

Meal #3, Time/Location _____
_____
_____
_____

Snack #3, Time/Location _____
_____

HOW DO YOU FEEL?
(Include Symptom/Time)
_____
_____
_____
_____
_____
_____
_____
_____
_____
_____
_____
_____
_____
_____
_____
_____
_____
_____
_____
_____
_____
_____
_____
_____
_____
_____
_____
_____
_____
_____
_____
_____

EXERCISE: What exercise did you do today? How long? How do you feel?
_____
_____
_____

WATER: Cross off each 8-ounce glass of water you drank today. (Mark other beverages with meals.)

1   2   3   4   5   6   7   8   9   10

LAST NIGHT'S SLEEP

When did you fall asleep last night? _____

When did you wake this morning? _____

How well did you sleep last night? (Rate from 1-10, with 10 being best) _____

Comments about sleep

_____
_____
_____
_____
_____
_____
_____
_____
_____
_____
_____
_____
_____
_____
_____
_____
_____
_____
_____

NEW MEDICATIONS/VITAMINS: List new medications. What side effects did you observe?

_____
_____
_____
_____
_____
_____
_____
_____
_____
_____
_____
_____
_____
_____

VITALS

Blood Sugar/Time _____/_____
Blood Sugar/Time _____/_____

Blood Pressure/Time _____/_____
Blood Pressure/Time _____/_____

Weight _____

BOWEL MOVEMENTS

BM No. 1/Time_____
BM Type (Circle) 1   2   3   4   5   6   7

Observations: _____
_____
_____

BM No. 2/Time_____
BM Type (Circle) 1   2   3   4   5   6   7

Observations: _____
_____
_____

BM No. 3/Time_____
BM Type (Circle) 1   2   3   4   5   6   7

Observations: _____
_____
_____

What challenge did you overcome today?

_____
_____
_____

What are you grateful for?

_____
_____
_____

What's the best thing that happened today?

_____
_____
_____

IT AIN'T JUST THE DIET
FOOD & WELLNESS DAILY LOG

Date: _____ Test Day #_____

Circle your suspected problem foods.
Common allergens: citrus, coffee, corn, dairy, eggs, fish/shellfish, gluten, meat (beef, lamb, pork), peanuts, raw fruits & vegetables, soy, tree nuts

WHAT DID YOU EAT TODAY?

Meal #1, Time/Location _____
_____
_____
_____

Snack #1, Time/Location _____
_____

Meal #2, Time/Location _____
_____
_____
_____

Snack #2, Time/Location _____
_____

Meal #3, Time/Location _____
_____
_____
_____

Snack #3, Time/Location _____
_____

EXERCISE: What exercise did you do today? How long? How do you feel?
_____
_____
_____

HOW DO YOU FEEL?
(Include Symptom/Time)
_____
_____
_____
_____
_____
_____
_____
_____
_____
_____
_____
_____
_____
_____
_____
_____
_____
_____
_____
_____
_____
_____
_____
_____
_____
_____
_____
_____
_____
_____
_____
_____
_____
_____
_____
_____
_____

WATER: Cross off each 8-ounce glass of water you drank today. (Mark other beverages with meals.)

1   2   3   4   5   6   7   8   9   10

LAST NIGHT'S SLEEP

When did you fall asleep last night? _____

When did you wake this morning? _____

How well did you sleep last night? (Rate from
1-10, with 10 being best) _____

Comments about sleep

_____
_____
_____
_____
_____
_____
_____
_____
_____
_____
_____
_____
_____
_____
_____
_____
_____
_____

NEW MEDICATIONS/VITAMINS: List new
medications. What side effects did you
observe?

_____
_____
_____
_____
_____
_____
_____
_____
_____
_____
_____
_____
_____

VITALS

Blood Sugar/Time _____/_____
Blood Sugar/Time _____/_____

Blood Pressure/Time _____/_____
Blood Pressure/Time _____/_____

Weight _____

BOWEL MOVEMENTS

BM No. 1/Time_____

BM Type (Circle) 1   2   3   4   5   6   7

Observations: _____
_____
_____

BM No. 2/Time_____

BM Type (Circle) 1   2   3   4   5   6   7

Observations: _____
_____
_____

BM No. 3/Time_____

BM Type (Circle) 1   2   3   4   5   6   7

Observations: _____
_____
_____

What challenge did you overcome today?

_____
_____
_____

What are you grateful for?

_____
_____
_____

What's the best thing that happened today?

_____
_____
_____

IT AIN'T JUST THE DIET
FOOD & WELLNESS DAILY LOG

Date: _____ Test Day #_____

Circle your suspected problem foods.
Common allergens: citrus, coffee, corn, dairy, eggs, fish/shellfish, gluten, meat (beef, lamb, pork), peanuts, raw fruits & vegetables, soy, tree nuts

WHAT DID YOU EAT TODAY?

Meal #1, Time/Location _____

_____

_____

_____

Snack #1, Time/Location _____

_____

_____

Meal #2, Time/Location _____

_____

_____

_____

Snack #2, Time/Location _____

_____

_____

Meal #3, Time/Location _____

_____

_____

_____

Snack #3, Time/Location _____

_____

HOW DO YOU FEEL?
(Include Symptom/Time)

_____
_____
_____
_____
_____
_____
_____
_____
_____
_____
_____
_____
_____
_____
_____
_____
_____
_____
_____
_____
_____
_____
_____
_____
_____
_____
_____
_____
_____
_____
_____
_____
_____
_____

EXERCISE: What exercise did you do today? How long? How do you feel?

_____
_____
_____

WATER: Cross off each 8-ounce glass of water you drank today. (Mark other beverages with meals.)

1   2   3   4   5   6   7   8   9   10

LAST NIGHT'S SLEEP

When did you fall asleep last night? _____

When did you wake this morning? _____

How well did you sleep last night? (Rate from 1-10, with 10 being best) _____

Comments about sleep

_____
_____
_____
_____
_____
_____
_____
_____
_____
_____
_____
_____
_____
_____
_____
_____
_____
_____
_____

NEW MEDICATIONS/VITAMINS: List new medications. What side effects did you observe?

_____
_____
_____
_____
_____
_____
_____
_____
_____
_____
_____
_____
_____

VITALS
Blood Sugar/Time _____/_____
Blood Sugar/Time _____/_____

Blood Pressure/Time _____/_____
Blood Pressure/Time _____/_____

Weight _____

BOWEL MOVEMENTS

BM No. 1/Time_____
BM Type (Circle) 1   2   3   4   5   6   7

Observations: _____
_____
_____

BM No. 2/Time_____
BM Type (Circle) 1   2   3   4   5   6   7

Observations: _____
_____
_____

BM No. 3/Time_____
BM Type (Circle) 1   2   3   4   5   6   7

Observations: _____
_____
_____

What challenge did you overcome today?
_____
_____
_____
_____

What are you grateful for?
_____
_____
_____
_____

What's the best thing that happened today?
_____
_____
_____
_____

IT AIN'T JUST THE DIET
FOOD & WELLNESS DAILY LOG

Date: _____ Test Day #_____

Circle your suspected problem foods.
Common allergens: citrus, coffee, corn, dairy, eggs, fish/shellfish, gluten, meat (beef, lamb, pork), peanuts, raw fruits & vegetables, soy, tree nuts

WHAT DID YOU EAT TODAY?

Meal #1, Time/Location _____
_____
_____
_____

Snack #1, Time/Location _____
_____
_____

Meal #2, Time/Location _____
_____
_____
_____

Snack #2, Time/Location _____
_____
_____

Meal #3, Time/Location _____
_____
_____
_____

Snack #3, Time/Location _____
_____
_____

HOW DO YOU FEEL?
(Include Symptom/Time)
_____
_____
_____
_____
_____
_____
_____
_____
_____
_____
_____
_____
_____
_____
_____
_____
_____
_____
_____
_____
_____
_____
_____
_____
_____
_____
_____
_____
_____
_____
_____
_____
_____
_____

EXERCISE: What exercise did you do today? How long? How do you feel?
_____
_____
_____

WATER: Cross off each 8-ounce glass of water you drank today. (Mark other beverages with meals.)

1   2   3   4   5   6   7   8   9   10

LAST NIGHT'S SLEEP

When did you fall asleep last night? _____

When did you wake this morning? _____

How well did you sleep last night? (Rate from 1-10, with 10 being best) _____

Comments about sleep

_____
_____
_____
_____
_____
_____
_____
_____
_____
_____
_____
_____
_____
_____
_____
_____
_____

NEW MEDICATIONS/VITAMINS: List new medications. What side effects did you observe?

_____
_____
_____
_____
_____
_____
_____
_____
_____
_____
_____
_____
_____
_____
_____
_____

VITALS
Blood Sugar/Time _____/_____
Blood Sugar/Time _____/_____

Blood Pressure/Time _____/_____
Blood Pressure/Time _____/_____

Weight _____

BOWEL MOVEMENTS

BM No. 1/Time_____
BM Type (Circle) 1 2 3 4 5 6 7

Observations: _____
_____
_____

BM No. 2/Time_____
BM Type (Circle) 1 2 3 4 5 6 7

Observations: _____
_____
_____

BM No. 3/Time_____
BM Type (Circle) 1 2 3 4 5 6 7

Observations: _____
_____
_____

What challenge did you overcome today?

_____
_____
_____

What are you grateful for?

_____
_____
_____

What's the best thing that happened today?

_____
_____
_____

IT AIN'T JUST THE DIET
FOOD & WELLNESS DAILY LOG

Date: _____ Test Day #_____

Circle your suspected problem foods.
Common allergens: citrus, coffee, corn, dairy, eggs, fish/shellfish, gluten, meat (beef, lamb, pork), peanuts, raw fruits & vegetables, soy, tree nuts

WHAT DID YOU EAT TODAY?

Meal #1, Time/Location _____
_____
_____
_____

Snack #1, Time/Location _____
_____
_____

Meal #2, Time/Location _____
_____
_____
_____

Snack #2, Time/Location _____
_____
_____

Meal #3, Time/Location _____
_____
_____
_____

Snack #3, Time/Location _____
_____
_____

HOW DO YOU FEEL?
(Include Symptom/Time)
_____
_____
_____
_____
_____
_____
_____
_____
_____
_____
_____
_____
_____
_____
_____
_____
_____
_____
_____
_____
_____
_____
_____
_____
_____
_____
_____
_____
_____
_____
_____
_____

EXERCISE: What exercise did you do today? How long? How do you feel?
_____
_____
_____

WATER: Cross off each 8-ounce glass of water you drank today. (Mark other beverages with meals.)

1   2   3   4   5   6   7   8   9   10

LAST NIGHT'S SLEEP

When did you fall asleep last night? _____

When did you wake this morning? _____

How well did you sleep last night? (Rate from 1-10, with 10 being best) _____

Comments about sleep

_____
_____
_____
_____
_____
_____
_____
_____
_____
_____
_____
_____
_____
_____
_____
_____
_____
_____
_____
_____
_____

NEW MEDICATIONS/VITAMINS: List new medications. What side effects did you observe?

_____
_____
_____
_____
_____
_____
_____
_____
_____
_____
_____
_____
_____
_____

VITALS

Blood Sugar/Time _____/_____
Blood Sugar/Time _____/_____

Blood Pressure/Time _____/_____
Blood Pressure/Time _____/_____

Weight _____

BOWEL MOVEMENTS

BM No. 1/Time_____
BM Type (Circle) 1   2   3   4   5   6   7

Observations: _____
_____
_____

BM No. 2/Time_____
BM Type (Circle) 1   2   3   4   5   6   7

Observations: _____
_____
_____

BM No. 3/Time_____
BM Type (Circle) 1   2   3   4   5   6   7

Observations: _____
_____
_____

What challenge did you overcome today?
_____
_____
_____

What are you grateful for?
_____
_____
_____

What's the best thing that happened today?
_____
_____
_____

Food Allergies, Sensitivities, & Intolerances Symptoms Checklist

Week 9 Assessment

Date: _____

Check each symptom you have experienced after eating (currently or in the recent past).

Breathing
- ☐ Sneezing
- ☐ Stuffy nose/sinuses
- ☐ Congestion
- ☐ Runny nose
- ☐ Face pain
- ☐ Difficulty breathing
- ☐ Wheezing or asthma

Skin
- ☐ Hives
- ☐ Eczema or rash
- ☐ Dandruff
- ☐ Ticklishness
- ☐ Flushing
- ☐ Rosy cheeks or ears

Eyes
- ☐ Itchy eyes
- ☐ Dry eyes

Digestive
- ☐ Bloating
- ☐ Gas
- ☐ Constipated
- ☐ Diarrhea or loose stools
- ☐ More bowel movements
- ☐ Fewer bowel movements
- ☐ Abdominal cramping
- ☐ Stinky bowel movements
- ☐ Undigested food in stool
- ☐ Bloody stool

Brain/Thinking
- ☐ Brain fog
- ☐ Inability to concentrate
- ☐ Disjointed or distractible thinking
- ☐ Headaches
- ☐ Glassy-eyed or spacey
- ☐ Trouble remembering things

Energy
- ☐ Hyperactivity
- ☐ Restlessness
- ☐ Tiredness/fatigue
- ☐ Low energy/activity

Difference in Sleep
- ☐ Better
- ☐ Worse
- ☐ Restless leg while sleeping
- ☐ Ideas why? _____

Pain
- ☐ Joint pain
- ☐ Muscle pain
- ☐ Other pain: _____

Mood
- ☐ Ecstatic
- ☐ Happy
- ☐ Neutral
- ☐ Sad
- ☐ Angry/Irritable
- ☐ Calm
- ☐ Anxious
- ☐ Feeling stressed (hair on fire)
- ☐ Filled with creativity
- ☐ Exhausted/no energy

Hunger Changes
- ☐ Craving certain foods (list) _____
- ☐ Hungry all the time
- ☐ Little or no interest in food

Other
- ☐ Bad breath
- ☐ Stinky feet
- ☐ Sweating hands/feet
- ☐ Other: _____

Notes:
_____
_____
_____
_____
_____
_____
_____
_____
_____
_____
_____

Week 9 Journal Prompt

What's the best thing that happened to you last week? Who did you share your success with?

_____
_____
_____
_____
_____
_____
_____
_____
_____
_____
_____
_____
_____
_____
_____
_____
_____
_____
_____
_____
_____
_____
_____
_____
_____
_____
_____
_____
_____
_____
_____
_____
_____
_____

IT AIN'T JUST THE DIET
FOOD & WELLNESS DAILY LOG

Date: _____   Test Day #_____

Circle your suspected problem foods.
Common allergens: citrus, coffee, corn, dairy, eggs, fish/shellfish, gluten, meat (beef, lamb, pork), peanuts, raw fruits & vegetables, soy, tree nuts

WHAT DID YOU EAT TODAY?

Meal #1, Time/Location _____
_____
_____
_____

Snack #1, Time/Location _____
_____
_____

Meal #2, Time/Location _____
_____
_____
_____

Snack #2, Time/Location _____
_____
_____

Meal #3, Time/Location _____
_____
_____
_____

Snack #3, Time/Location _____
_____
_____

EXERCISE: What exercise did you do today? How long? How do you feel?
_____
_____
_____

HOW DO YOU FEEL?
(Include Symptom/Time)
_____
_____
_____
_____
_____
_____
_____
_____
_____
_____
_____
_____
_____
_____
_____
_____
_____
_____
_____
_____
_____
_____
_____
_____
_____
_____
_____
_____
_____
_____
_____
_____
_____
_____
_____
_____
_____

WATER: Cross off each 8-ounce glass of water you drank today. (Mark other beverages with meals.)

1   2   3   4   5   6   7   8   9   10

LAST NIGHT'S SLEEP

When did you fall asleep last night? _____

When did you wake this morning? _____

How well did you sleep last night? (Rate from 1-10, with 10 being best) _____

Comments about sleep

_____
_____
_____
_____
_____
_____
_____
_____
_____
_____
_____
_____
_____
_____
_____
_____
_____
_____

NEW MEDICATIONS/VITAMINS: List new medications. What side effects did you observe?

_____
_____
_____
_____
_____
_____
_____
_____
_____
_____
_____
_____
_____
_____

VITALS

Blood Sugar/Time _____/_____
Blood Sugar/Time _____/_____

Blood Pressure/Time _____/_____
Blood Pressure/Time _____/_____

Weight _____

BOWEL MOVEMENTS

BM No. 1/Time_____
BM Type (Circle) 1   2   3   4   5   6   7

Observations: _____
_____
_____

BM No. 2/Time_____
BM Type (Circle) 1   2   3   4   5   6   7

Observations: _____
_____
_____

BM No. 3/Time_____
BM Type (Circle) 1   2   3   4   5   6   7

Observations: _____
_____
_____

What challenge did you overcome today?
_____
_____
_____

What are you grateful for?
_____
_____
_____

What's the best thing that happened today?
_____
_____
_____

IT AIN'T JUST THE DIET
FOOD & WELLNESS DAILY LOG

Date: _____ Test Day #_____

Circle your suspected problem foods.
Common allergens: citrus, coffee, corn, dairy, eggs, fish/shellfish, gluten, meat (beef, lamb, pork), peanuts, raw fruits & vegetables, soy, tree nuts

WHAT DID YOU EAT TODAY?

Meal #1, Time/Location _____
_____
_____
_____

Snack #1, Time/Location _____
_____
_____

Meal #2, Time/Location _____
_____
_____
_____

Snack #2, Time/Location _____
_____
_____

Meal #3, Time/Location _____
_____
_____
_____

Snack #3, Time/Location _____
_____
_____

HOW DO YOU FEEL?
(Include Symptom/Time)
_____
_____
_____
_____
_____
_____
_____
_____
_____
_____
_____
_____
_____
_____
_____
_____
_____
_____
_____
_____
_____
_____
_____
_____
_____
_____
_____
_____
_____
_____
_____
_____
_____
_____
_____
_____
_____
_____

EXERCISE: What exercise did you do today? How long? How do you feel?
_____
_____
_____

WATER: Cross off each 8-ounce glass of water you drank today. (Mark other beverages with meals.)

1   2   3   4   5   6   7   8   9   10

LAST NIGHT'S SLEEP

When did you fall asleep last night? _____

When did you wake this morning? _____

How well did you sleep last night? (Rate from 1-10, with 10 being best) _____

Comments about sleep

_____
_____
_____
_____
_____
_____
_____
_____
_____
_____
_____
_____
_____
_____
_____
_____
_____
_____
_____

NEW MEDICATIONS/VITAMINS: List new medications. What side effects did you observe?

_____
_____
_____
_____
_____
_____
_____
_____
_____
_____
_____
_____
_____
_____
_____

VITALS

Blood Sugar/Time _____/_____
Blood Sugar/Time _____/_____

Blood Pressure/Time _____/_____
Blood Pressure/Time _____/_____

Weight _____

BOWEL MOVEMENTS

BM No. 1/Time_____
BM Type (Circle) 1   2   3   4   5   6   7

Observations: _____
_____
_____

BM No. 2/Time_____
BM Type (Circle) 1   2   3   4   5   6   7

Observations: _____
_____
_____

BM No. 3/Time_____
BM Type (Circle) 1   2   3   4   5   6   7

Observations: _____
_____
_____

What challenge did you overcome today?
_____
_____
_____

What are you grateful for?
_____
_____
_____

What's the best thing that happened today?
_____
_____
_____

IT AIN'T JUST THE DIET
FOOD & WELLNESS DAILY LOG

Date: _____ Test Day #_____

Circle your suspected problem foods.
Common allergens: citrus, coffee, corn, dairy, eggs, fish/shellfish, gluten, meat (beef, lamb, pork), peanuts, raw fruits & vegetables, soy, tree nuts

WHAT DID YOU EAT TODAY?

Meal #1, Time/Location _____
_____
_____
_____
_____

Snack #1, Time/Location _____
_____
_____

Meal #2, Time/Location _____
_____
_____
_____
_____

Snack #2, Time/Location _____
_____
_____

Meal #3, Time/Location _____
_____
_____
_____
_____

Snack #3, Time/Location _____
_____
_____

HOW DO YOU FEEL?
(Include Symptom/Time)
_____
_____
_____
_____
_____
_____
_____
_____
_____
_____
_____
_____
_____
_____
_____
_____
_____
_____
_____
_____
_____
_____
_____
_____
_____
_____
_____
_____
_____
_____
_____
_____
_____
_____
_____
_____

EXERCISE: What exercise did you do today? How long? How do you feel?
_____
_____
_____

WATER: Cross off each 8-ounce glass of water you drank today. (Mark other beverages with meals.)

1   2   3   4   5   6   7   8   9   10

LAST NIGHT'S SLEEP

When did you fall asleep last night? _____

When did you wake this morning? _____

How well did you sleep last night? (Rate from 1-10, with 10 being best) _____

Comments about sleep

_____
_____
_____
_____
_____
_____
_____
_____
_____
_____
_____
_____
_____
_____
_____
_____
_____

NEW MEDICATIONS/VITAMINS: List new medications. What side effects did you observe?

_____
_____
_____
_____
_____
_____
_____
_____
_____
_____
_____
_____
_____
_____
_____
_____

VITALS

Blood Sugar/Time _____ / _____
Blood Sugar/Time _____ / _____

Blood Pressure/Time _____ / _____
Blood Pressure/Time _____ / _____

Weight _____

BOWEL MOVEMENTS

BM No. 1/Time_____
BM Type (Circle) 1   2   3   4   5   6   7

Observations: _____
_____
_____

BM No. 2/Time_____
BM Type (Circle) 1   2   3   4   5   6   7

Observations: _____
_____
_____

BM No. 3/Time_____
BM Type (Circle) 1   2   3   4   5   6   7

Observations: _____
_____

What challenge did you overcome today?
_____
_____
_____

What are you grateful for?
_____
_____
_____

What's the best thing that happened today?
_____
_____
_____

IT AIN'T JUST THE DIET
FOOD & WELLNESS DAILY LOG

Date: _____ Test Day #_____

Circle your suspected problem foods.
Common allergens: citrus, coffee, corn, dairy, eggs, fish/shellfish, gluten, meat (beef, lamb, pork), peanuts, raw fruits & vegetables, soy, tree nuts

WHAT DID YOU EAT TODAY?

Meal #1, Time/Location _____
_____
_____
_____

Snack #1, Time/Location _____
_____
_____

Meal #2, Time/Location _____
_____
_____
_____

Snack #2, Time/Location _____
_____
_____

Meal #3, Time/Location _____
_____
_____
_____

Snack #3, Time/Location _____
_____
_____

HOW DO YOU FEEL?
(Include Symptom/Time)
_____
_____
_____
_____
_____
_____
_____
_____
_____
_____
_____
_____
_____
_____
_____
_____
_____
_____
_____
_____
_____
_____
_____
_____
_____
_____
_____
_____
_____
_____
_____
_____
_____
_____
_____
_____

EXERCISE: What exercise did you do today? How long? How do you feel?
_____
_____
_____

WATER: Cross off each 8-ounce glass of water you drank today. (Mark other beverages with meals.)

1 2 3 4 5 6 7 8 9 10

LAST NIGHT'S SLEEP

When did you fall asleep last night? _____

When did you wake this morning? _____

How well did you sleep last night? (Rate from 1-10, with 10 being best) _____

Comments about sleep

_____
_____
_____
_____
_____
_____
_____
_____
_____
_____
_____
_____
_____
_____
_____
_____
_____
_____

NEW MEDICATIONS/VITAMINS: List new medications. What side effects did you observe?

_____
_____
_____
_____
_____
_____
_____
_____
_____
_____
_____
_____
_____
_____

VITALS

Blood Sugar/Time _____/_____
Blood Sugar/Time _____/_____

Blood Pressure/Time _____/_____
Blood Pressure/Time _____/_____

Weight _____

BOWEL MOVEMENTS

BM No. 1/Time_____
BM Type (Circle) 1   2   3   4   5   6   7

Observations: _____
_____
_____

BM No. 2/Time_____
BM Type (Circle) 1   2   3   4   5   6   7

Observations: _____
_____
_____

BM No. 3/Time_____
BM Type (Circle) 1   2   3   4   5   6   7

Observations: _____
_____
_____

What challenge did you overcome today?
_____
_____
_____

What are you grateful for?
_____
_____
_____

What's the best thing that happened today?
_____
_____
_____

IT AIN'T JUST THE DIET
FOOD & WELLNESS DAILY LOG

Date: _____ Test Day #_____

Circle your suspected problem foods.
Common allergens: citrus, coffee, corn, dairy, eggs, fish/shellfish, gluten, meat (beef, lamb, pork), peanuts, raw fruits & vegetables, soy, tree nuts

WHAT DID YOU EAT TODAY?

Meal #1, Time/Location _____
_____
_____
_____

Snack #1, Time/Location _____
_____

Meal #2, Time/Location _____
_____
_____
_____

Snack #2, Time/Location _____
_____

Meal #3, Time/Location _____
_____
_____
_____

Snack #3, Time/Location _____
_____

EXERCISE: What exercise did you do today? How long? How do you feel?
_____
_____
_____

HOW DO YOU FEEL?
(Include Symptom/Time)
_____
_____
_____
_____
_____
_____
_____
_____
_____
_____
_____
_____
_____
_____
_____
_____
_____
_____
_____
_____
_____
_____
_____
_____
_____
_____
_____
_____
_____
_____
_____
_____
_____
_____
_____
_____

WATER: Cross off each 8-ounce glass of water you drank today. (Mark other beverages with meals.)

1   2   3   4   5   6   7   8   9   10

LAST NIGHT'S SLEEP

When did you fall asleep last night? _____

When did you wake this morning? _____

How well did you sleep last night? (Rate from 1-10, with 10 being best) _____

Comments about sleep

_____
_____
_____
_____
_____
_____
_____
_____
_____
_____
_____
_____
_____
_____
_____
_____
_____
_____

NEW MEDICATIONS/VITAMINS: List new medications. What side effects did you observe?

_____
_____
_____
_____
_____
_____
_____
_____
_____
_____
_____
_____
_____

VITALS

Blood Sugar/Time _____/_____
Blood Sugar/Time _____/_____

Blood Pressure/Time _____/_____
Blood Pressure/Time _____/_____

Weight _____

BOWEL MOVEMENTS

BM No. 1/Time_____
BM Type (Circle) 1   2   3   4   5   6   7

Observations: _____
_____
_____

BM No. 2/Time_____
BM Type (Circle) 1   2   3   4   5   6   7

Observations: _____
_____
_____

BM No. 3/Time_____
BM Type (Circle) 1   2   3   4   5   6   7

Observations: _____
_____
_____

What challenge did you overcome today?

_____
_____
_____

What are you grateful for?

_____
_____
_____

What's the best thing that happened today?

_____
_____
_____

IT AIN'T JUST THE DIET
FOOD & WELLNESS DAILY LOG

Date: _____ Test Day #_____

Circle your suspected problem foods.
Common allergens: citrus, coffee, corn, dairy, eggs, fish/shellfish, gluten, meat (beef, lamb, pork), peanuts, raw fruits & vegetables, soy, tree nuts

WHAT DID YOU EAT TODAY?

Meal #1, Time/Location _____
_____
_____
_____

Snack #1, Time/Location _____
_____
_____

Meal #2, Time/Location _____
_____
_____
_____

Snack #2, Time/Location _____
_____
_____

Meal #3, Time/Location _____
_____
_____
_____

Snack #3, Time/Location _____
_____
_____

HOW DO YOU FEEL?
(Include Symptom/Time)
_____
_____
_____
_____
_____
_____
_____
_____
_____
_____
_____
_____
_____
_____
_____
_____
_____
_____
_____
_____
_____
_____
_____
_____
_____
_____
_____
_____
_____
_____
_____
_____

EXERCISE: What exercise did you do today? How long? How do you feel?
_____
_____
_____

WATER: Cross off each 8-ounce glass of water you drank today. (Mark other beverages with meals.)

1   2   3   4   5   6   7   8   9   10

LAST NIGHT'S SLEEP

When did you fall asleep last night? _____

When did you wake this morning? _____

How well did you sleep last night? (Rate from 1-10, with 10 being best) _____

Comments about sleep

_____
_____
_____
_____
_____
_____
_____
_____
_____
_____
_____
_____
_____
_____
_____
_____
_____
_____
_____

NEW MEDICATIONS/VITAMINS: List new medications. What side effects did you observe?

_____
_____
_____
_____
_____
_____
_____
_____
_____
_____
_____
_____
_____
_____

VITALS

Blood Sugar/Time _____ / _____
Blood Sugar/Time _____ / _____

Blood Pressure/Time _____ / _____
Blood Pressure/Time _____ / _____

Weight _____

BOWEL MOVEMENTS

BM No. 1/Time_____
BM Type (Circle) 1   2   3   4   5   6   7

Observations: _____
_____
_____

BM No. 2/Time_____
BM Type (Circle) 1   2   3   4   5   6   7

Observations: _____
_____
_____

BM No. 3/Time_____
BM Type (Circle) 1   2   3   4   5   6   7

Observations: _____
_____
_____

What challenge did you overcome today?
_____
_____
_____

What are you grateful for?
_____
_____
_____

What's the best thing that happened today?
_____
_____
_____

IT AIN'T JUST THE DIET
FOOD & WELLNESS DAILY LOG

Date: _____ Test Day #_____

Circle your suspected problem foods.
Common allergens: citrus, coffee, corn, dairy, eggs, fish/shellfish, gluten, meat (beef, lamb, pork), peanuts, raw fruits & vegetables, soy, tree nuts

WHAT DID YOU EAT TODAY?

Meal #1, Time/Location _____
_____
_____
_____

Snack #1, Time/Location _____
_____
_____

Meal #2, Time/Location _____
_____
_____
_____

Snack #2, Time/Location _____
_____
_____

Meal #3, Time/Location _____
_____
_____
_____

Snack #3, Time/Location _____
_____
_____

HOW DO YOU FEEL?
(Include Symptom/Time)
_____
_____
_____
_____
_____
_____
_____
_____
_____
_____
_____
_____
_____
_____
_____
_____
_____
_____
_____
_____
_____
_____
_____
_____
_____
_____
_____
_____
_____
_____
_____
_____
_____
_____
_____
_____
_____

EXERCISE: What exercise did you do today? How long? How do you feel?
_____
_____
_____

WATER: Cross off each 8-ounce glass of water you drank today. (Mark other beverages with meals.)

1   2   3   4   5   6   7   8   9   10

LAST NIGHT'S SLEEP

When did you fall asleep last night? _____

When did you wake this morning? _____

How well did you sleep last night? (Rate from 1-10, with 10 being best) _____

Comments about sleep

_____
_____
_____
_____
_____
_____
_____
_____
_____
_____
_____
_____
_____
_____
_____
_____
_____
_____

NEW MEDICATIONS/VITAMINS: List new medications. What side effects did you observe?

_____
_____
_____
_____
_____
_____
_____
_____
_____
_____
_____
_____
_____
_____

VITALS

Blood Sugar/Time _____/_____
Blood Sugar/Time _____/_____

Blood Pressure/Time _____/_____
Blood Pressure/Time _____/_____

Weight _____

BOWEL MOVEMENTS

BM No. 1/Time_____
BM Type (Circle) 1   2   3   4   5   6   7

Observations: _____
_____
_____

BM No. 2/Time_____
BM Type (Circle) 1   2   3   4   5   6   7

Observations: _____
_____
_____

BM No. 3/Time_____
BM Type (Circle) 1   2   3   4   5   6   7

Observations: _____
_____
_____

What challenge did you overcome today?
_____
_____
_____

What are you grateful for?
_____
_____
_____

What's the best thing that happened today?
_____
_____
_____

Food Allergies, Sensitivities, & Intolerances Symptoms Checklist

Week 10 Assessment

Date: _____

Check each symptom you have experienced after eating (currently or in the recent past).

Breathing
- ☐ Sneezing
- ☐ Stuffy nose/sinuses
- ☐ Congestion
- ☐ Runny nose
- ☐ Face pain
- ☐ Difficulty breathing
- ☐ Wheezing or asthma

Skin
- ☐ Hives
- ☐ Eczema or rash
- ☐ Dandruff
- ☐ Ticklishness
- ☐ Flushing
- ☐ Rosy cheeks or ears

Eyes
- ☐ Itchy eyes
- ☐ Dry eyes

Digestive
- ☐ Bloating
- ☐ Gas
- ☐ Constipated
- ☐ Diarrhea or loose stools
- ☐ More bowel movements
- ☐ Fewer bowel movements
- ☐ Abdominal cramping
- ☐ Stinky bowel movements
- ☐ Undigested food in stool
- ☐ Bloody stool

Brain/Thinking
- ☐ Brain fog
- ☐ Inability to concentrate
- ☐ Disjointed or distractible thinking
- ☐ Headaches
- ☐ Glassy-eyed or spacey
- ☐ Trouble remembering things

Energy
- ☐ Hyperactivity
- ☐ Restlessness
- ☐ Tiredness/fatigue
- ☐ Low energy/activity

Difference in Sleep
- ☐ Better
- ☐ Worse
- ☐ Restless leg while sleeping
- ☐ Ideas why? _____

Pain
- ☐ Joint pain
- ☐ Muscle pain
- ☐ Other pain: _____

Mood
- ☐ Ecstatic
- ☐ Happy
- ☐ Neutral
- ☐ Sad
- ☐ Angry/Irritable
- ☐ Calm
- ☐ Anxious
- ☐ Feeling stressed (hair on fire)
- ☐ Filled with creativity
- ☐ Exhausted/no energy

Hunger Changes
- ☐ Craving certain foods (list) _____
- ☐ Hungry all the time
- ☐ Little or no interest in food

Other
- ☐ Bad breath
- ☐ Stinky feet
- ☐ Sweating hands/feet
- ☐ Other: _____

Notes:
_____
_____
_____
_____
_____
_____
_____
_____
_____
_____
_____

Week 10 Journal Prompt

How do you keep yourself calm and unstressed? Do you exercise? Do deep breathing? Meditate? Do yoga? Talk to a friend? Take a bath? Take a bath with a friend? ;-)

_____
_____
_____
_____
_____
_____
_____
_____
_____
_____
_____
_____
_____
_____
_____
_____
_____
_____
_____
_____
_____
_____
_____
_____
_____
_____
_____
_____

IT AIN'T JUST THE DIET
FOOD & WELLNESS DAILY LOG

Date: _____ Test Day #_____

Circle your suspected problem foods.
Common allergens: citrus, coffee, corn, dairy, eggs, fish/shellfish, gluten, meat (beef, lamb, pork), peanuts, raw fruits & vegetables, soy, tree nuts

WHAT DID YOU EAT TODAY?

Meal #1, Time/Location _____
_____
_____
_____

Snack #1, Time/Location _____
_____
_____

Meal #2, Time/Location _____
_____
_____
_____

Snack #2, Time/Location _____
_____
_____

Meal #3, Time/Location _____
_____
_____
_____

Snack #3, Time/Location _____
_____
_____

HOW DO YOU FEEL?
(Include Symptom/Time)
_____
_____
_____
_____
_____
_____
_____
_____
_____
_____
_____
_____
_____
_____
_____
_____
_____
_____
_____
_____
_____
_____
_____
_____
_____
_____
_____
_____
_____
_____
_____
_____
_____
_____

EXERCISE: What exercise did you do today? How long? How do you feel?
_____
_____
_____

WATER: Cross off each 8-ounce glass of water you drank today. (Mark other beverages with meals.)

1   2   3   4   5   6   7   8   9   10

LAST NIGHT'S SLEEP

When did you fall asleep last night? _____

When did you wake this morning? _____

How well did you sleep last night? (Rate from 1-10, with 10 being best) _____

Comments about sleep

_____
_____
_____
_____
_____
_____
_____
_____
_____
_____
_____
_____
_____
_____
_____
_____
_____
_____

NEW MEDICATIONS/VITAMINS: List new medications. What side effects did you observe?

_____
_____
_____
_____
_____
_____
_____
_____
_____
_____
_____
_____
_____
_____
_____
_____

VITALS

Blood Sugar/Time _____/_____
Blood Sugar/Time _____/_____

Blood Pressure/Time _____/_____
Blood Pressure/Time _____/_____

Weight _____

BOWEL MOVEMENTS

BM No. 1/Time_____
BM Type (Circle) 1　2　3　4　5　6　7

Observations: _____
_____
_____

BM No. 2/Time_____
BM Type (Circle) 1　2　3　4　5　6　7

Observations: _____
_____
_____

BM No. 3/Time_____
BM Type (Circle) 1　2　3　4　5　6　7

Observations: _____
_____
_____

What challenge did you overcome today?

_____
_____
_____

What are you grateful for?

_____
_____
_____

What's the best thing that happened today?

_____
_____
_____

IT AIN'T JUST THE DIET
FOOD & WELLNESS DAILY LOG

Date: _____ Test Day #_____

Circle your suspected problem foods.
Common allergens: citrus, coffee, corn, dairy, eggs, fish/shellfish, gluten, meat (beef, lamb, pork), peanuts, raw fruits & vegetables, soy, tree nuts

WHAT DID YOU EAT TODAY?

Meal #1, Time/Location _____
_____
_____
_____

Snack #1, Time/Location _____
_____
_____

Meal #2, Time/Location _____
_____
_____
_____

Snack #2, Time/Location _____
_____
_____

Meal #3, Time/Location _____
_____
_____
_____

Snack #3, Time/Location _____
_____
_____

HOW DO YOU FEEL?
(Include Symptom/Time)
_____
_____
_____
_____
_____
_____
_____
_____
_____
_____
_____
_____
_____
_____
_____
_____
_____
_____
_____
_____
_____
_____
_____
_____
_____
_____
_____
_____
_____
_____
_____
_____
_____
_____

EXERCISE: What exercise did you do today? How long? How do you feel?
_____
_____
_____

WATER: Cross off each 8-ounce glass of water you drank today. (Mark other beverages with meals.)

1   2   3   4   5   6   7   8   9   10

LAST NIGHT'S SLEEP

When did you fall asleep last night? _____

When did you wake this morning? _____

How well did you sleep last night? (Rate from
1-10, with 10 being best) _____

Comments about sleep

_____
_____
_____
_____
_____
_____
_____
_____
_____
_____
_____
_____
_____
_____
_____
_____
_____
_____

NEW MEDICATIONS/VITAMINS: List new
medications. What side effects did you
observe?

_____
_____
_____
_____
_____
_____
_____
_____
_____
_____
_____
_____
_____

VITALS

Blood Sugar/Time _____/_____
Blood Sugar/Time _____/_____

Blood Pressure/Time _____/_____
Blood Pressure/Time _____/_____

Weight _____

BOWEL MOVEMENTS

BM No. 1/Time_____
BM Type (Circle) 1   2   3   4   5   6   7

Observations: _____
_____
_____

BM No. 2/Time_____
BM Type (Circle) 1   2   3   4   5   6   7

Observations: _____
_____
_____

BM No. 3/Time_____
BM Type (Circle) 1   2   3   4   5   6   7

Observations: _____
_____
_____

What challenge did you overcome today?

_____
_____
_____

What are you grateful for?

_____
_____
_____

What's the best thing that happened today?

_____
_____
_____

IT AIN'T JUST THE DIET
FOOD & WELLNESS DAILY LOG

Date: _____ Test Day #_____

Circle your suspected problem foods.
Common allergens: citrus, coffee, corn, dairy,
eggs, fish/shellfish, gluten, meat (beef, lamb,
pork), peanuts, raw fruits & vegetables, soy,
tree nuts

WHAT DID YOU EAT TODAY?

Meal #1, Time/Location _____
_____
_____
_____

Snack #1, Time/Location _____
_____

Meal #2, Time/Location _____
_____
_____
_____

Snack #2, Time/Location _____
_____

Meal #3, Time/Location _____
_____
_____
_____

Snack #3, Time/Location _____
_____

EXERCISE: What exercise did you do today?
How long? How do you feel?
_____
_____
_____

HOW DO YOU FEEL?
(Include Symptom/Time)
_____
_____
_____
_____
_____
_____
_____
_____
_____
_____
_____
_____
_____
_____
_____
_____
_____
_____
_____
_____
_____
_____
_____
_____
_____
_____
_____
_____
_____
_____
_____
_____
_____
_____
_____
_____
_____
_____

WATER: Cross off each 8-ounce glass of water
you drank today. (Mark other beverages with
meals.)

1   2   3   4   5   6   7   8   9   10

LAST NIGHT'S SLEEP

When did you fall asleep last night? _____

When did you wake this morning? _____

How well did you sleep last night? (Rate from 1-10, with 10 being best) _____

Comments about sleep

_____
_____
_____
_____
_____
_____
_____
_____
_____
_____
_____
_____
_____
_____
_____
_____
_____
_____
_____
_____
_____
_____

NEW MEDICATIONS/VITAMINS: List new medications. What side effects did you observe?

_____
_____
_____
_____
_____
_____
_____
_____
_____
_____
_____
_____
_____
_____
_____

VITALS

Blood Sugar/Time _____/_____
Blood Sugar/Time _____/_____

Blood Pressure/Time _____/_____
Blood Pressure/Time _____/_____

Weight _____

BOWEL MOVEMENTS

BM No. 1/Time_____
BM Type (Circle) 1   2   3   4   5   6   7

Observations: _____
_____
_____

BM No. 2/Time_____
BM Type (Circle) 1   2   3   4   5   6   7

Observations: _____
_____
_____

BM No. 3/Time_____
BM Type (Circle) 1   2   3   4   5   6   7

Observations: _____
_____
_____

What challenge did you overcome today?

_____
_____
_____

What are you grateful for?

_____
_____
_____

What's the best thing that happened today?

_____
_____
_____

IT AIN'T JUST THE DIET
FOOD & WELLNESS DAILY LOG

Date: _____ Test Day #_____

Circle your suspected problem foods.
Common allergens: citrus, coffee, corn, dairy,
eggs, fish/shellfish, gluten, meat (beef, lamb,
pork), peanuts, raw fruits & vegetables, soy,
tree nuts

WHAT DID YOU EAT TODAY?

Meal #1, Time/Location _____
_____
_____
_____

Snack #1, Time/Location _____
_____
_____

Meal #2, Time/Location _____
_____
_____
_____

Snack #2, Time/Location _____
_____
_____

Meal #3, Time/Location _____
_____
_____
_____

Snack #3, Time/Location _____
_____
_____

EXERCISE: What exercise did you do today?
How long? How do you feel?
_____
_____
_____

HOW DO YOU FEEL?
(Include Symptom/Time)
_____
_____
_____
_____
_____
_____
_____
_____
_____
_____
_____
_____
_____
_____
_____
_____
_____
_____
_____
_____
_____
_____
_____
_____
_____
_____
_____
_____
_____
_____
_____
_____
_____
_____

WATER: Cross off each 8-ounce glass of water
you drank today. (Mark other beverages with
meals.)

1   2   3   4   5   6   7   8   9   10

LAST NIGHT'S SLEEP

When did you fall asleep last night? _____

When did you wake this morning? _____

How well did you sleep last night? (Rate from 1-10, with 10 being best) _____

Comments about sleep

_____
_____
_____
_____
_____
_____
_____
_____
_____
_____
_____
_____
_____
_____
_____
_____
_____
_____
_____

NEW MEDICATIONS/VITAMINS: List new medications. What side effects did you observe?

_____
_____
_____
_____
_____
_____
_____
_____
_____
_____
_____
_____
_____
_____
_____

VITALS

Blood Sugar/Time _____/_____
Blood Sugar/Time _____/_____

Blood Pressure/Time _____/_____
Blood Pressure/Time _____/_____

Weight _____

BOWEL MOVEMENTS

BM No. 1/Time_____
BM Type (Circle) 1 2 3 4 5 6 7

Observations: _____
_____
_____

BM No. 2/Time_____
BM Type (Circle) 1 2 3 4 5 6 7

Observations: _____
_____
_____

BM No. 3/Time_____
BM Type (Circle) 1 2 3 4 5 6 7

Observations: _____
_____
_____

What challenge did you overcome today?

_____
_____
_____
_____

What are you grateful for?

_____
_____
_____
_____

What's the best thing that happened today?

_____
_____
_____
_____

IT AIN'T JUST THE DIET
FOOD & WELLNESS DAILY LOG

Date: _____ Test Day #_____

Circle your suspected problem foods.
Common allergens: citrus, coffee, corn, dairy, eggs, fish/shellfish, gluten, meat (beef, lamb, pork), peanuts, raw fruits & vegetables, soy, tree nuts

WHAT DID YOU EAT TODAY?

Meal #1, Time/Location _____
_____
_____
_____

Snack #1, Time/Location _____
_____
_____

Meal #2, Time/Location _____
_____
_____
_____

Snack #2, Time/Location _____
_____
_____

Meal #3, Time/Location _____
_____
_____
_____

Snack #3, Time/Location _____
_____
_____

EXERCISE: What exercise did you do today? How long? How do you feel?
_____
_____
_____

HOW DO YOU FEEL?
(Include Symptom/Time)
_____
_____
_____
_____
_____
_____
_____
_____
_____
_____
_____
_____
_____
_____
_____
_____
_____
_____
_____
_____
_____
_____
_____
_____
_____
_____
_____
_____
_____
_____
_____
_____
_____
_____

WATER: Cross off each 8-ounce glass of water you drank today. (Mark other beverages with meals.)

1 2 3 4 5 6 7 8 9 10

LAST NIGHT'S SLEEP

When did you fall asleep last night? _____

When did you wake this morning? _____

How well did you sleep last night? (Rate from 1-10, with 10 being best) _____

Comments about sleep

_____
_____
_____
_____
_____
_____
_____
_____
_____
_____
_____
_____
_____
_____
_____
_____
_____
_____

NEW MEDICATIONS/VITAMINS: List new medications. What side effects did you observe?

_____
_____
_____
_____
_____
_____
_____
_____
_____
_____
_____
_____
_____
_____
_____

VITALS

Blood Sugar/Time _____/_____
Blood Sugar/Time _____/_____

Blood Pressure/Time _____/_____
Blood Pressure/Time _____/_____

Weight _____

BOWEL MOVEMENTS

BM No. 1/Time_____
BM Type (Circle) 1   2   3   4   5   6   7

Observations: _____
_____
_____

BM No. 2/Time_____
BM Type (Circle) 1   2   3   4   5   6   7

Observations: _____
_____
_____

BM No. 3/Time_____
BM Type (Circle) 1   2   3   4   5   6   7

Observations: _____
_____
_____

What challenge did you overcome today?
_____
_____
_____

What are you grateful for?
_____
_____
_____

What's the best thing that happened today?
_____
_____
_____

IT AIN'T JUST THE DIET
FOOD & WELLNESS DAILY LOG

Date: _____ Test Day #_____

Circle your suspected problem foods.
Common allergens: citrus, coffee, corn, dairy, eggs, fish/shellfish, gluten, meat (beef, lamb, pork), peanuts, raw fruits & vegetables, soy, tree nuts

WHAT DID YOU EAT TODAY?

Meal #1, Time/Location _____
_____
_____
_____

Snack #1, Time/Location _____
_____

Meal #2, Time/Location _____
_____
_____
_____

Snack #2, Time/Location _____
_____

Meal #3, Time/Location _____
_____
_____
_____

Snack #3, Time/Location _____
_____

HOW DO YOU FEEL?
(Include Symptom/Time)

_____
_____
_____
_____
_____
_____
_____
_____
_____
_____
_____
_____
_____
_____
_____
_____
_____
_____
_____
_____
_____
_____
_____
_____
_____
_____
_____
_____
_____
_____
_____

EXERCISE: What exercise did you do today? How long? How do you feel?
_____
_____
_____

WATER: Cross off each 8-ounce glass of water you drank today. (Mark other beverages with meals.)

1   2   3   4   5   6   7   8   9   10

LAST NIGHT'S SLEEP

When did you fall asleep last night? _____

When did you wake this morning? _____

How well did you sleep last night? (Rate from 1-10, with 10 being best) _____

Comments about sleep

_____
_____
_____
_____
_____
_____
_____
_____
_____
_____
_____
_____
_____
_____
_____
_____
_____
_____
_____
_____
_____
_____

NEW MEDICATIONS/VITAMINS: List new medications. What side effects did you observe?

_____
_____
_____
_____
_____
_____
_____
_____
_____
_____
_____
_____
_____
_____
_____

VITALS

Blood Sugar/Time _____/_____
Blood Sugar/Time _____/_____

Blood Pressure/Time _____/_____
Blood Pressure/Time _____/_____

Weight _____

BOWEL MOVEMENTS

BM No. 1/Time_____
BM Type (Circle) 1   2   3   4   5   6   7

Observations: _____
_____
_____

BM No. 2/Time_____
BM Type (Circle) 1   2   3   4   5   6   7

Observations: _____
_____
_____

BM No. 3/Time_____
BM Type (Circle) 1   2   3   4   5   6   7

Observations: _____
_____
_____

What challenge did you overcome today?
_____
_____
_____
_____

What are you grateful for?
_____
_____
_____
_____

What's the best thing that happened today?
_____
_____
_____
_____

IT AIN'T JUST THE DIET
FOOD & WELLNESS DAILY LOG

Date: _____ Test Day #_____

Circle your suspected problem foods.
Common allergens: citrus, coffee, corn, dairy, eggs, fish/shellfish, gluten, meat (beef, lamb, pork), peanuts, raw fruits & vegetables, soy, tree nuts

WHAT DID YOU EAT TODAY?

Meal #1, Time/Location _____
_____
_____
_____

Snack #1, Time/Location _____
_____
_____

Meal #2, Time/Location _____
_____
_____
_____

Snack #2, Time/Location _____
_____
_____

Meal #3, Time/Location _____
_____
_____
_____

Snack #3, Time/Location _____
_____
_____

HOW DO YOU FEEL?
(Include Symptom/Time)
_____
_____
_____
_____
_____
_____
_____
_____
_____
_____
_____
_____
_____
_____
_____
_____
_____
_____
_____
_____
_____
_____
_____
_____
_____
_____
_____
_____
_____
_____
_____
_____
_____
_____
_____

EXERCISE: What exercise did you do today? How long? How do you feel?
_____
_____
_____

WATER: Cross off each 8-ounce glass of water you drank today. (Mark other beverages with meals.)

1   2   3   4   5   6   7   8   9   10

LAST NIGHT'S SLEEP

When did you fall asleep last night? _____

When did you wake this morning? _____

How well did you sleep last night? (Rate from 1-10, with 10 being best) _____

Comments about sleep

_____
_____
_____
_____
_____
_____
_____
_____
_____
_____
_____
_____
_____
_____
_____
_____
_____
_____
_____
_____
_____

NEW MEDICATIONS/VITAMINS: List new medications. What side effects did you observe?

_____
_____
_____
_____
_____
_____
_____
_____
_____
_____
_____
_____
_____
_____
_____
_____

VITALS
Blood Sugar/Time _____/_____
Blood Sugar/Time _____/_____

Blood Pressure/Time _____/_____
Blood Pressure/Time _____/_____

Weight _____

BOWEL MOVEMENTS

BM No. 1/Time_____
BM Type (Circle) 1   2   3   4   5   6   7

Observations: _____
_____
_____

BM No. 2/Time_____
BM Type (Circle) 1   2   3   4   5   6   7

Observations: _____
_____
_____

BM No. 3/Time_____
BM Type (Circle) 1   2   3   4   5   6   7

Observations: _____
_____
_____

What challenge did you overcome today?
_____
_____
_____
_____

What are you grateful for?
_____
_____
_____
_____

What's the best thing that happened today?
_____
_____
_____
_____

Food Allergies, Sensitivities, & Intolerances Symptoms Checklist

Week 11 Assessment

Date: _____

Check each symptom you have experienced after eating (currently or in the recent past).

Breathing
- ☐ Sneezing
- ☐ Stuffy nose/sinuses
- ☐ Congestion
- ☐ Runny nose
- ☐ Face pain
- ☐ Difficulty breathing
- ☐ Wheezing or asthma

Skin
- ☐ Hives
- ☐ Eczema or rash
- ☐ Dandruff
- ☐ Ticklishness
- ☐ Flushing
- ☐ Rosy cheeks or ears

Eyes
- ☐ Itchy eyes
- ☐ Dry eyes

Digestive
- ☐ Bloating
- ☐ Gas
- ☐ Constipated
- ☐ Diarrhea or loose stools
- ☐ More bowel movements
- ☐ Fewer bowel movements
- ☐ Abdominal cramping
- ☐ Stinky bowel movements
- ☐ Undigested food in stool
- ☐ Bloody stool

Brain/Thinking
- ☐ Brain fog
- ☐ Inability to concentrate
- ☐ Disjointed or distractible thinking
- ☐ Headaches
- ☐ Glassy-eyed or spacey
- ☐ Trouble remembering things

Energy
- ☐ Hyperactivity
- ☐ Restlessness
- ☐ Tiredness/fatigue
- ☐ Low energy/activity

Difference in Sleep
- ☐ Better
- ☐ Worse
- ☐ Restless leg while sleeping
- ☐ Ideas why? _____

Pain
- ☐ Joint pain
- ☐ Muscle pain
- ☐ Other pain: _____

Mood
- ☐ Ecstatic
- ☐ Happy
- ☐ Neutral
- ☐ Sad
- ☐ Angry/Irritable
- ☐ Calm
- ☐ Anxious
- ☐ Feeling stressed (hair on fire)
- ☐ Filled with creativity
- ☐ Exhausted/no energy

Hunger Changes
- ☐ Craving certain foods (list) _____
- ☐ Hungry all the time
- ☐ Little or no interest in food

Other
- ☐ Bad breath
- ☐ Stinky feet
- ☐ Sweating hands/feet
- ☐ Other: _____

Notes:
_____
_____
_____
_____
_____
_____
_____
_____
_____
_____
_____

Week 11 Journal Prompt

Do you have health goals? What are they? How do you keep yourself motivated toward your goals?

_____
_____
_____
_____
_____
_____
_____
_____
_____
_____
_____
_____
_____
_____
_____
_____
_____
_____
_____
_____
_____
_____
_____
_____
_____
_____
_____
_____
_____
_____

IT AIN'T JUST THE DIET
FOOD & WELLNESS DAILY LOG

Date: _____ Test Day #_____

Circle your suspected problem foods.
Common allergens: citrus, coffee, corn, dairy, eggs, fish/shellfish, gluten, meat (beef, lamb, pork), peanuts, raw fruits & vegetables, soy, tree nuts

WHAT DID YOU EAT TODAY?

Meal #1, Time/Location _____
_____
_____
_____

Snack #1, Time/Location _____
_____
_____

Meal #2, Time/Location _____
_____
_____
_____

Snack #2, Time/Location _____
_____
_____

Meal #3, Time/Location _____
_____
_____
_____

Snack #3, Time/Location _____
_____
_____

HOW DO YOU FEEL?
(Include Symptom/Time)
_____
_____
_____
_____
_____
_____
_____
_____
_____
_____
_____
_____
_____
_____
_____
_____
_____
_____
_____
_____
_____
_____
_____
_____
_____
_____
_____
_____
_____
_____
_____
_____
_____
_____
_____

EXERCISE: What exercise did you do today? How long? How do you feel?
_____
_____
_____

WATER: Cross off each 8-ounce glass of water you drank today. (Mark other beverages with meals.)

1   2   3   4   5   6   7   8   9   10

LAST NIGHT'S SLEEP

When did you fall asleep last night? _____

When did you wake this morning? _____

How well did you sleep last night? (Rate from 1-10, with 10 being best) _____

Comments about sleep

_____
_____
_____
_____
_____
_____
_____
_____
_____
_____
_____
_____
_____
_____
_____
_____
_____
_____

NEW MEDICATIONS/VITAMINS: List new medications. What side effects did you observe?

_____
_____
_____
_____
_____
_____
_____
_____
_____
_____
_____
_____
_____
_____

VITALS

Blood Sugar/Time _____/_____
Blood Sugar/Time _____/_____

Blood Pressure/Time _____/_____
Blood Pressure/Time _____/_____

Weight _____

BOWEL MOVEMENTS

BM No. 1/Time_____
BM Type (Circle) 1   2   3   4   5   6   7

Observations: _____
_____
_____

BM No. 2/Time_____
BM Type (Circle) 1   2   3   4   5   6   7

Observations: _____
_____
_____

BM No. 3/Time_____
BM Type (Circle) 1   2   3   4   5   6   7

Observations: _____
_____
_____

What challenge did you overcome today?
_____
_____
_____

What are you grateful for?
_____
_____
_____

What's the best thing that happened today?
_____
_____
_____

IT AIN'T JUST THE DIET
FOOD & WELLNESS DAILY LOG

Date: _____ Test Day #_____

Circle your suspected problem foods.
Common allergens: citrus, coffee, corn, dairy, eggs, fish/shellfish, gluten, meat (beef, lamb, pork), peanuts, raw fruits & vegetables, soy, tree nuts

WHAT DID YOU EAT TODAY?

Meal #1, Time/Location _____
_____
_____
_____

Snack #1, Time/Location _____
_____
_____

Meal #2, Time/Location _____
_____
_____
_____

Snack #2, Time/Location _____
_____
_____

Meal #3, Time/Location _____
_____
_____
_____

Snack #3, Time/Location _____
_____

HOW DO YOU FEEL?
(Include Symptom/Time)
_____
_____
_____
_____
_____
_____
_____
_____
_____
_____
_____
_____
_____
_____
_____
_____
_____
_____
_____
_____
_____
_____
_____
_____
_____
_____
_____
_____
_____
_____
_____

EXERCISE: What exercise did you do today? How long? How do you feel?
_____
_____

WATER: Cross off each 8-ounce glass of water you drank today. (Mark other beverages with meals.)

1   2   3   4   5   6   7   8   9   10

LAST NIGHT'S SLEEP

When did you fall asleep last night? _____

When did you wake this morning? _____

How well did you sleep last night? (Rate from 1-10, with 10 being best) _____

Comments about sleep

_____
_____
_____
_____
_____
_____
_____
_____
_____
_____
_____
_____
_____
_____
_____
_____
_____
_____
_____
_____

NEW MEDICATIONS/VITAMINS: List new medications. What side effects did you observe?

_____
_____
_____
_____
_____
_____
_____
_____
_____
_____
_____
_____
_____
_____

VITALS

Blood Sugar/Time _____/_____
Blood Sugar/Time _____/_____

Blood Pressure/Time _____/_____
Blood Pressure/Time _____/_____

Weight _____

BOWEL MOVEMENTS

BM No. 1/Time_____
BM Type (Circle) 1   2   3   4   5   6   7

Observations: _____
_____
_____

BM No. 2/Time_____
BM Type (Circle) 1   2   3   4   5   6   7

Observations: _____
_____
_____

BM No. 3/Time_____
BM Type (Circle) 1   2   3   4   5   6   7

Observations: _____
_____
_____

What challenge did you overcome today?

_____
_____
_____
_____

What are you grateful for?

_____
_____
_____
_____

What's the best thing that happened today?

_____
_____
_____
_____

IT AIN'T JUST THE DIET
FOOD & WELLNESS DAILY LOG

Date: _____ Test Day #_____

Circle your suspected problem foods.
Common allergens: citrus, coffee, corn, dairy, eggs, fish/shellfish, gluten, meat (beef, lamb, pork), peanuts, raw fruits & vegetables, soy, tree nuts

WHAT DID YOU EAT TODAY?

Meal #1, Time/Location _____
_____
_____
_____

Snack #1, Time/Location _____
_____
_____

Meal #2, Time/Location _____
_____
_____
_____

Snack #2, Time/Location _____
_____
_____

Meal #3, Time/Location _____
_____
_____
_____

Snack #3, Time/Location _____
_____
_____

HOW DO YOU FEEL?
(Include Symptom/Time)
_____
_____
_____
_____
_____
_____
_____
_____
_____
_____
_____
_____
_____
_____
_____
_____
_____
_____
_____
_____
_____
_____
_____
_____
_____
_____
_____
_____
_____
_____
_____
_____
_____
_____
_____

EXERCISE: What exercise did you do today? How long? How do you feel?
_____
_____
_____

WATER: Cross off each 8-ounce glass of water you drank today. (Mark other beverages with meals.)

1   2   3   4   5   6   7   8   9   10

LAST NIGHT'S SLEEP

When did you fall asleep last night? _____

When did you wake this morning? _____

How well did you sleep last night? (Rate from 1-10, with 10 being best) _____

Comments about sleep

_____
_____
_____
_____
_____
_____
_____
_____
_____
_____
_____
_____
_____
_____
_____
_____
_____
_____

NEW MEDICATIONS/VITAMINS: List new medications. What side effects did you observe?

_____
_____
_____
_____
_____
_____
_____
_____
_____
_____
_____
_____
_____
_____
_____

VITALS

Blood Sugar/Time _____/_____
Blood Sugar/Time _____/_____

Blood Pressure/Time _____/_____
Blood Pressure/Time _____/_____

Weight _____

BOWEL MOVEMENTS

BM No. 1/Time_____
BM Type (Circle) 1   2   3   4   5   6   7

Observations: _____
_____
_____

BM No. 2/Time_____
BM Type (Circle) 1   2   3   4   5   6   7

Observations: _____
_____
_____

BM No. 3/Time_____
BM Type (Circle) 1   2   3   4   5   6   7

Observations: _____
_____
_____

What challenge did you overcome today?
_____
_____
_____

What are you grateful for?
_____
_____
_____

What's the best thing that happened today?
_____
_____
_____

IT AIN'T JUST THE DIET
FOOD & WELLNESS DAILY LOG

Date: _____ Test Day # _____

Circle your suspected problem foods.
Common allergens: citrus, coffee, corn, dairy, eggs, fish/shellfish, gluten, meat (beef, lamb, pork), peanuts, raw fruits & vegetables, soy, tree nuts

WHAT DID YOU EAT TODAY?

Meal #1, Time/Location _____
_____
_____
_____

Snack #1, Time/Location _____
_____

Meal #2, Time/Location _____
_____
_____
_____

Snack #2, Time/Location _____
_____

Meal #3, Time/Location _____
_____
_____
_____

Snack #3, Time/Location _____
_____
_____

HOW DO YOU FEEL?
(Include Symptom/Time)

_____
_____
_____
_____
_____
_____
_____
_____
_____
_____
_____
_____
_____
_____
_____
_____
_____
_____
_____
_____
_____
_____
_____
_____
_____
_____
_____
_____
_____
_____
_____
_____
_____
_____
_____
_____
_____
_____
_____
_____
_____

EXERCISE: What exercise did you do today? How long? How do you feel?
_____
_____
_____

WATER: Cross off each 8-ounce glass of water you drank today. (Mark other beverages with meals.)

1   2   3   4   5   6   7   8   9   10

LAST NIGHT'S SLEEP

When did you fall asleep last night? _____

When did you wake this morning? _____

How well did you sleep last night? (Rate from 1-10, with 10 being best) _____

Comments about sleep

_____
_____
_____
_____
_____
_____
_____
_____
_____
_____
_____
_____
_____
_____
_____
_____
_____
_____
_____

NEW MEDICATIONS/VITAMINS: List new medications. What side effects did you observe?

_____
_____
_____
_____
_____
_____
_____
_____
_____
_____
_____
_____
_____
_____

VITALS

Blood Sugar/Time _____ / _____
Blood Sugar/Time _____ / _____

Blood Pressure/Time _____ / _____
Blood Pressure/Time _____ / _____

Weight _____

BOWEL MOVEMENTS

BM No. 1/Time_____
BM Type (Circle) 1   2   3   4   5   6   7

Observations: _____
_____
_____

BM No. 2/Time_____
BM Type (Circle) 1   2   3   4   5   6   7

Observations: _____
_____
_____

BM No. 3/Time_____
BM Type (Circle) 1   2   3   4   5   6   7

Observations: _____
_____
_____

What challenge did you overcome today?

_____
_____
_____
_____

What are you grateful for?

_____
_____
_____
_____

What's the best thing that happened today?

_____
_____
_____
_____

IT AIN'T JUST THE DIET
FOOD & WELLNESS DAILY LOG

Date: _____ Test Day #_____

Circle your suspected problem foods.
Common allergens: citrus, coffee, corn, dairy, eggs, fish/shellfish, gluten, meat (beef, lamb, pork), peanuts, raw fruits & vegetables, soy, tree nuts

WHAT DID YOU EAT TODAY?

Meal #1, Time/Location _____
_____
_____
_____

Snack #1, Time/Location _____
_____
_____

Meal #2, Time/Location _____
_____
_____
_____

Snack #2, Time/Location _____
_____
_____

Meal #3, Time/Location _____
_____
_____
_____

Snack #3, Time/Location _____
_____
_____

HOW DO YOU FEEL?
(Include Symptom/Time)
_____
_____
_____
_____
_____
_____
_____
_____
_____
_____
_____
_____
_____
_____
_____
_____
_____
_____
_____
_____
_____
_____
_____
_____
_____
_____
_____
_____
_____
_____
_____
_____
_____
_____

EXERCISE: What exercise did you do today? How long? How do you feel?
_____
_____
_____

WATER: Cross off each 8-ounce glass of water you drank today. (Mark other beverages with meals.)

1   2   3   4   5   6   7   8   9   10

LAST NIGHT'S SLEEP

When did you fall asleep last night? _____

When did you wake this morning? _____

How well did you sleep last night? (Rate from 1-10, with 10 being best) _____

Comments about sleep

_____
_____
_____
_____
_____
_____
_____
_____
_____
_____
_____
_____
_____
_____
_____
_____
_____
_____
_____

NEW MEDICATIONS/VITAMINS: List new medications. What side effects did you observe?

_____
_____
_____
_____
_____
_____
_____
_____
_____
_____
_____
_____
_____
_____

VITALS

Blood Sugar/Time _____ / _____
Blood Sugar/Time _____ / _____

Blood Pressure/Time _____ / _____
Blood Pressure/Time _____ / _____

Weight _____

BOWEL MOVEMENTS

BM No. 1/Time_____
BM Type (Circle) 1   2   3   4   5   6   7

Observations: _____
_____
_____

BM No. 2/Time_____
BM Type (Circle) 1   2   3   4   5   6   7

Observations: _____
_____
_____

BM No. 3/Time_____
BM Type (Circle) 1   2   3   4   5   6   7

Observations: _____
_____
_____

What challenge did you overcome today?
_____
_____
_____

What are you grateful for?
_____
_____
_____

What's the best thing that happened today?
_____
_____
_____

IT AIN'T JUST THE DIET
FOOD & WELLNESS DAILY LOG

Date: _____ Test Day #_____

Circle your suspected problem foods.
Common allergens: citrus, coffee, corn, dairy, eggs, fish/shellfish, gluten, meat (beef, lamb, pork), peanuts, raw fruits & vegetables, soy, tree nuts

WHAT DID YOU EAT TODAY?

Meal #1, Time/Location _____
_____
_____
_____

Snack #1, Time/Location _____
_____
_____

Meal #2, Time/Location _____
_____
_____
_____

Snack #2, Time/Location _____
_____
_____

Meal #3, Time/Location _____
_____
_____
_____

Snack #3, Time/Location _____
_____
_____

EXERCISE: What exercise did you do today? How long? How do you feel?
_____
_____
_____

HOW DO YOU FEEL?
(Include Symptom/Time)
_____
_____
_____
_____
_____
_____
_____
_____
_____
_____
_____
_____
_____
_____
_____
_____
_____
_____
_____
_____
_____
_____
_____
_____
_____
_____
_____
_____
_____
_____
_____
_____
_____
_____

WATER: Cross off each 8-ounce glass of water you drank today. (Mark other beverages with meals.)

1   2   3   4   5   6   7   8   9   10

LAST NIGHT'S SLEEP

When did you fall asleep last night? _____

When did you wake this morning? _____

How well did you sleep last night? (Rate from 1-10, with 10 being best) _____

Comments about sleep

_____
_____
_____
_____
_____
_____
_____
_____
_____
_____
_____
_____
_____
_____
_____
_____
_____
_____
_____
_____
_____
_____

NEW MEDICATIONS/VITAMINS: List new medications. What side effects did you observe?

_____
_____
_____
_____
_____
_____
_____
_____
_____
_____
_____
_____
_____
_____

VITALS

Blood Sugar/Time _____/_____
Blood Sugar/Time _____/_____

Blood Pressure/Time _____/_____
Blood Pressure/Time _____/_____

Weight _____

BOWEL MOVEMENTS

BM No. 1/Time_____
BM Type (Circle) 1   2   3   4   5   6   7

Observations: _____
_____
_____

BM No. 2/Time_____
BM Type (Circle) 1   2   3   4   5   6   7

Observations: _____
_____
_____

BM No. 3/Time_____
BM Type (Circle) 1   2   3   4   5   6   7

Observations: _____
_____
_____

What challenge did you overcome today?
_____
_____
_____
_____

What are you grateful for?
_____
_____
_____

What's the best thing that happened today?
_____
_____
_____

IT AIN'T JUST THE DIET
FOOD & WELLNESS DAILY LOG

Date: _____ Test Day #_____

Circle your suspected problem foods.
Common allergens: citrus, coffee, corn, dairy, eggs, fish/shellfish, gluten, meat (beef, lamb, pork), peanuts, raw fruits & vegetables, soy, tree nuts

WHAT DID YOU EAT TODAY?

Meal #1, Time/Location _____
_____
_____
_____

Snack #1, Time/Location _____
_____
_____

Meal #2, Time/Location _____
_____
_____
_____

Snack #2, Time/Location _____
_____
_____

Meal #3, Time/Location _____
_____
_____
_____

Snack #3, Time/Location _____
_____

HOW DO YOU FEEL?
(Include Symptom/Time)
_____
_____
_____
_____
_____
_____
_____
_____
_____
_____
_____
_____
_____
_____
_____
_____
_____
_____
_____
_____
_____
_____
_____
_____
_____
_____
_____
_____
_____
_____
_____
_____
_____
_____
_____
_____
_____

EXERCISE: What exercise did you do today? How long? How do you feel?
_____
_____
_____

WATER: Cross off each 8-ounce glass of water you drank today. (Mark other beverages with meals.)

1   2   3   4   5   6   7   8   9   10

LAST NIGHT'S SLEEP

When did you fall asleep last night? _____

When did you wake this morning? _____

How well did you sleep last night? (Rate from 1-10, with 10 being best) _____

Comments about sleep

_____
_____
_____
_____
_____
_____
_____
_____
_____
_____
_____
_____
_____
_____
_____
_____
_____
_____
_____

NEW MEDICATIONS/VITAMINS: List new medications. What side effects did you observe?

_____
_____
_____
_____
_____
_____
_____
_____
_____
_____
_____
_____
_____
_____
_____
_____

VITALS

Blood Sugar/Time _____/_____
Blood Sugar/Time _____/_____

Blood Pressure/Time _____/_____
Blood Pressure/Time _____/_____

Weight _____

BOWEL MOVEMENTS

BM No. 1/Time_____

BM Type (Circle) 1 2 3 4 5 6 7

Observations: _____
_____
_____

BM No. 2/Time_____

BM Type (Circle) 1 2 3 4 5 6 7

Observations: _____
_____
_____

BM No. 3/Time_____

BM Type (Circle) 1 2 3 4 5 6 7

Observations: _____
_____
_____

What challenge did you overcome today?

_____
_____
_____

What are you grateful for?

_____
_____
_____

What's the best thing that happened today?

_____
_____
_____

Food Allergies, Sensitivities, & Intolerances Symptoms Checklist

Week 12 Assessment

Date: _____

Check each symptom you have experienced after eating (currently or in the recent past).

Breathing
- ☐ Sneezing
- ☐ Stuffy nose/sinuses
- ☐ Congestion
- ☐ Runny nose
- ☐ Face pain
- ☐ Difficulty breathing
- ☐ Wheezing or asthma

Skin
- ☐ Hives
- ☐ Eczema or rash
- ☐ Dandruff
- ☐ Ticklishness
- ☐ Flushing
- ☐ Rosy cheeks or ears

Eyes
- ☐ Itchy eyes
- ☐ Dry eyes

Digestive
- ☐ Bloating
- ☐ Gas
- ☐ Constipated
- ☐ Diarrhea or loose stools
- ☐ More bowel movements
- ☐ Fewer bowel movements
- ☐ Abdominal cramping
- ☐ Stinky bowel movements
- ☐ Undigested food in stool
- ☐ Bloody stool

Brain/Thinking
- ☐ Brain fog
- ☐ Inability to concentrate
- ☐ Disjointed or distractible thinking
- ☐ Headaches
- ☐ Glassy-eyed or spacey
- ☐ Trouble remembering things

Energy
- ☐ Hyperactivity
- ☐ Restlessness
- ☐ Tiredness/fatigue
- ☐ Low energy/activity

Difference in Sleep
- ☐ Better
- ☐ Worse
- ☐ Restless leg while sleeping
- ☐ Ideas why? _____

Pain
- ☐ Joint pain
- ☐ Muscle pain
- ☐ Other pain: _____

Mood
- ☐ Ecstatic
- ☐ Happy
- ☐ Neutral
- ☐ Sad
- ☐ Angry/Irritable
- ☐ Calm
- ☐ Anxious
- ☐ Feeling stressed (hair on fire)
- ☐ Filled with creativity
- ☐ Exhausted/no energy

Hunger Changes
- ☐ Craving certain foods (list) _____
- ☐ Hungry all the time
- ☐ Little or no interest in food

Other
- ☐ Bad breath
- ☐ Stinky feet
- ☐ Sweating hands/feet
- ☐ Other: _____

Notes:
_____
_____
_____
_____
_____
_____
_____
_____
_____
_____
_____

Week 12 Journal Prompt

How will you continue your pathway to better health?

_____
_____
_____
_____
_____
_____
_____
_____
_____
_____
_____
_____
_____
_____
_____
_____
_____
_____
_____
_____
_____
_____
_____
_____
_____
_____
_____
_____
_____
_____
_____
_____

IT AIN'T JUST THE DIET
FOOD & WELLNESS DAILY LOG

Date: _____ Test Day #_____

Circle your suspected problem foods.
Common allergens: citrus, coffee, corn, dairy, eggs, fish/shellfish, gluten, meat (beef, lamb, pork), peanuts, raw fruits & vegetables, soy, tree nuts

WHAT DID YOU EAT TODAY?

Meal #1, Time/Location _____
_____
_____
_____

Snack #1, Time/Location _____
_____
_____

Meal #2, Time/Location _____
_____
_____
_____

Snack #2, Time/Location _____
_____
_____

Meal #3, Time/Location _____
_____
_____
_____

Snack #3, Time/Location _____
_____
_____

HOW DO YOU FEEL?
(Include Symptom/Time)
_____
_____
_____
_____
_____
_____
_____
_____
_____
_____
_____
_____
_____
_____
_____
_____
_____
_____
_____
_____
_____
_____
_____
_____
_____
_____
_____
_____
_____
_____
_____
_____
_____
_____

EXERCISE: What exercise did you do today? How long? How do you feel?
_____
_____

WATER: Cross off each 8-ounce glass of water you drank today. (Mark other beverages with meals.)

1   2   3   4   5   6   7   8   9   10

LAST NIGHT'S SLEEP

When did you fall asleep last night? _____

When did you wake this morning? _____

How well did you sleep last night? (Rate from 1-10, with 10 being best) _____

Comments about sleep

_____
_____
_____
_____
_____
_____
_____
_____
_____
_____
_____
_____
_____
_____
_____
_____
_____
_____
_____
_____
_____

NEW MEDICATIONS/VITAMINS: List new medications. What side effects did you observe?

_____
_____
_____
_____
_____
_____
_____
_____
_____
_____
_____
_____
_____
_____
_____

VITALS

Blood Sugar/Time _____/_____
Blood Sugar/Time _____/_____

Blood Pressure/Time _____/_____
Blood Pressure/Time _____/_____

Weight _____

BOWEL MOVEMENTS

BM No. 1/Time_____
BM Type (Circle) 1   2   3   4   5   6   7

Observations: _____
_____
_____

BM No. 2/Time_____
BM Type (Circle) 1   2   3   4   5   6   7

Observations: _____
_____
_____

BM No. 3/Time_____
BM Type (Circle) 1   2   3   4   5   6   7

Observations: _____
_____
_____

What challenge did you overcome today?

_____
_____
_____

What are you grateful for?

_____
_____
_____

What's the best thing that happened today?

_____
_____
_____

IT AIN'T JUST THE DIET
FOOD & WELLNESS DAILY LOG

Date: _____ Test Day #_____

Circle your suspected problem foods.
Common allergens: citrus, coffee, corn, dairy, eggs, fish/shellfish, gluten, meat (beef, lamb, pork), peanuts, raw fruits & vegetables, soy, tree nuts

WHAT DID YOU EAT TODAY?

Meal #1, Time/Location _____
_____
_____
_____
_____

Snack #1, Time/Location _____
_____
_____

Meal #2, Time/Location _____
_____
_____
_____
_____

Snack #2, Time/Location _____
_____
_____

Meal #3, Time/Location _____
_____
_____
_____
_____

Snack #3, Time/Location _____
_____
_____

EXERCISE: What exercise did you do today? How long? How do you feel?
_____
_____
_____

HOW DO YOU FEEL?
(Include Symptom/Time)
_____
_____
_____
_____
_____
_____
_____
_____
_____
_____
_____
_____
_____
_____
_____
_____
_____
_____
_____
_____
_____
_____
_____
_____
_____
_____
_____
_____
_____
_____
_____
_____
_____
_____
_____
_____
_____
_____
_____
_____

WATER: Cross off each 8-ounce glass of water you drank today. (Mark other beverages with meals.)

1   2   3   4   5   6   7   8   9   10

LAST NIGHT'S SLEEP

When did you fall asleep last night? _____

When did you wake this morning? _____

How well did you sleep last night? (Rate from 1-10, with 10 being best) _____

Comments about sleep

_____
_____
_____
_____
_____
_____
_____
_____
_____
_____
_____
_____
_____
_____
_____
_____
_____
_____
_____

NEW MEDICATIONS/VITAMINS: List new medications. What side effects did you observe?

_____
_____
_____
_____
_____
_____
_____
_____
_____
_____
_____
_____
_____

VITALS

Blood Sugar/Time _____/_____
Blood Sugar/Time _____/_____

Blood Pressure/Time _____/_____
Blood Pressure/Time _____/_____

Weight _____

BOWEL MOVEMENTS

BM No. 1/Time_____
BM Type (Circle) 1   2   3   4   5   6   7

Observations: _____
_____
_____

BM No. 2/Time_____
BM Type (Circle) 1   2   3   4   5   6   7

Observations: _____
_____
_____

BM No. 3/Time_____
BM Type (Circle) 1   2   3   4   5   6   7

Observations: _____
_____
_____

What challenge did you overcome today?
_____
_____
_____

What are you grateful for?
_____
_____
_____

What's the best thing that happened today?
_____
_____
_____

IT AIN'T JUST THE DIET
FOOD & WELLNESS DAILY LOG

Date: _____ Test Day #_____

Circle your suspected problem foods.
Common allergens: citrus, coffee, corn, dairy,
eggs, fish/shellfish, gluten, meat (beef, lamb,
pork), peanuts, raw fruits & vegetables, soy,
tree nuts

WHAT DID YOU EAT TODAY?

Meal #1, Time/Location _____
_____
_____
_____

Snack #1, Time/Location _____
_____
_____

Meal #2, Time/Location _____
_____
_____
_____

Snack #2, Time/Location _____
_____
_____

Meal #3, Time/Location _____
_____
_____
_____

Snack #3, Time/Location _____
_____
_____

HOW DO YOU FEEL?
(Include Symptom/Time)
_____
_____
_____
_____
_____
_____
_____
_____
_____
_____
_____
_____
_____
_____
_____
_____
_____
_____
_____
_____
_____
_____
_____
_____
_____
_____
_____
_____
_____
_____
_____
_____
_____

EXERCISE: What exercise did you do today?
How long? How do you feel?
_____
_____
_____

WATER: Cross off each 8-ounce glass of water
you drank today. (Mark other beverages with
meals.)

1   2   3   4   5   6   7   8   9   10

LAST NIGHT'S SLEEP

When did you fall asleep last night? _____

When did you wake this morning? _____

How well did you sleep last night? (Rate from 1-10, with 10 being best) _____

Comments about sleep

_____
_____
_____
_____
_____
_____
_____
_____
_____
_____
_____
_____
_____
_____
_____
_____
_____
_____
_____
_____

NEW MEDICATIONS/VITAMINS: List new medications. What side effects did you observe?

_____
_____
_____
_____
_____
_____
_____
_____
_____
_____
_____
_____
_____
_____
_____

VITALS

Blood Sugar/Time _____/_____
Blood Sugar/Time _____/_____

Blood Pressure/Time _____/_____
Blood Pressure/Time _____/_____

Weight _____

BOWEL MOVEMENTS

BM No. 1/Time_____
BM Type (Circle) 1   2   3   4   5   6   7

Observations: _____
_____
_____

BM No. 2/Time_____
BM Type (Circle) 1   2   3   4   5   6   7

Observations: _____
_____
_____

BM No. 3/Time_____
BM Type (Circle) 1   2   3   4   5   6   7

Observations: _____
_____
_____

What challenge did you overcome today?

_____
_____
_____

What are you grateful for?

_____
_____
_____

What's the best thing that happened today?

_____
_____
_____

IT AIN'T JUST THE DIET
FOOD & WELLNESS DAILY LOG

Date: _____ Test Day #_____

Circle your suspected problem foods.
Common allergens: citrus, coffee, corn, dairy, eggs, fish/shellfish, gluten, meat (beef, lamb, pork), peanuts, raw fruits & vegetables, soy, tree nuts

WHAT DID YOU EAT TODAY?

Meal #1, Time/Location _____
_____
_____
_____

Snack #1, Time/Location _____
_____
_____

Meal #2, Time/Location _____
_____
_____
_____

Snack #2, Time/Location _____
_____
_____

Meal #3, Time/Location _____
_____
_____
_____

Snack #3, Time/Location _____
_____
_____

EXERCISE: What exercise did you do today? How long? How do you feel?
_____
_____
_____

HOW DO YOU FEEL?
(Include Symptom/Time)
_____
_____
_____
_____
_____
_____
_____
_____
_____
_____
_____
_____
_____
_____
_____
_____
_____
_____
_____
_____
_____
_____
_____
_____
_____
_____
_____
_____
_____
_____
_____
_____
_____
_____
_____
_____

WATER: Cross off each 8-ounce glass of water you drank today. (Mark other beverages with meals.)

1   2   3   4   5   6   7   8   9   10

LAST NIGHT'S SLEEP

When did you fall asleep last night? _____

When did you wake this morning? _____

How well did you sleep last night? (Rate from 1-10, with 10 being best) _____

Comments about sleep

_____
_____
_____
_____
_____
_____
_____
_____
_____
_____
_____
_____
_____
_____
_____
_____
_____

NEW MEDICATIONS/VITAMINS: List new medications. What side effects did you observe?

_____
_____
_____
_____
_____
_____
_____
_____
_____
_____
_____
_____
_____
_____
_____
_____

VITALS
Blood Sugar/Time _____/_____
Blood Sugar/Time _____/_____

Blood Pressure/Time _____/_____
Blood Pressure/Time _____/_____

Weight _____

BOWEL MOVEMENTS

BM No. 1/Time_____
BM Type (Circle) 1   2   3   4   5   6   7

Observations: _____
_____
_____

BM No. 2/Time_____
BM Type (Circle) 1   2   3   4   5   6   7

Observations: _____
_____
_____

BM No. 3/Time_____
BM Type (Circle) 1   2   3   4   5   6   7

Observations: _____
_____
_____

What challenge did you overcome today?
_____
_____
_____

What are you grateful for?
_____
_____
_____

What's the best thing that happened today?
_____
_____
_____

IT AIN'T JUST THE DIET
FOOD & WELLNESS DAILY LOG

Date: _____ Test Day #_____

Circle your suspected problem foods.
Common allergens: citrus, coffee, corn, dairy, eggs, fish/shellfish, gluten, meat (beef, lamb, pork), peanuts, raw fruits & vegetables, soy, tree nuts

WHAT DID YOU EAT TODAY?

Meal #1, Time/Location _____
_____
_____
_____
_____

Snack #1, Time/Location _____
_____
_____

Meal #2, Time/Location _____
_____
_____
_____
_____

Snack #2, Time/Location _____
_____
_____

Meal #3, Time/Location _____
_____
_____
_____
_____

Snack #3, Time/Location _____
_____
_____

HOW DO YOU FEEL?
(Include Symptom/Time)
_____
_____
_____
_____
_____
_____
_____
_____
_____
_____
_____
_____
_____
_____
_____
_____
_____
_____
_____
_____
_____
_____
_____
_____
_____
_____
_____
_____
_____
_____
_____
_____
_____
_____
_____

EXERCISE: What exercise did you do today? How long? How do you feel?
_____
_____
_____

WATER: Cross off each 8-ounce glass of water you drank today. (Mark other beverages with meals.)

1   2   3   4   5   6   7   8   9   10

LAST NIGHT'S SLEEP

When did you fall asleep last night? _____

When did you wake this morning? _____

How well did you sleep last night? (Rate from 1-10, with 10 being best) _____

Comments about sleep

_____
_____
_____
_____
_____
_____
_____
_____
_____
_____
_____
_____
_____
_____
_____
_____
_____
_____
_____
_____

NEW MEDICATIONS/VITAMINS: List new medications. What side effects did you observe?

_____
_____
_____
_____
_____
_____
_____
_____
_____
_____
_____
_____
_____
_____
_____
_____

VITALS

Blood Sugar/Time _____/_____
Blood Sugar/Time _____/_____

Blood Pressure/Time _____/_____
Blood Pressure/Time _____/_____

Weight _____

BOWEL MOVEMENTS

BM No. 1/Time_____
BM Type (Circle) 1   2   3   4   5   6   7

Observations: _____
_____
_____

BM No. 2/Time_____
BM Type (Circle) 1   2   3   4   5   6   7

Observations: _____
_____
_____

BM No. 3/Time_____
BM Type (Circle) 1   2   3   4   5   6   7

Observations: _____
_____
_____

What challenge did you overcome today?

_____
_____
_____

What are you grateful for?

_____
_____
_____

What's the best thing that happened today?

_____
_____
_____

IT AIN'T JUST THE DIET
FOOD & WELLNESS DAILY LOG

Date: _____ Test Day #_____

Circle your suspected problem foods.
Common allergens: citrus, coffee, corn, dairy, eggs, fish/shellfish, gluten, meat (beef, lamb, pork), peanuts, raw fruits & vegetables, soy, tree nuts

WHAT DID YOU EAT TODAY?

Meal #1, Time/Location _____
_____
_____
_____

Snack #1, Time/Location _____
_____
_____

Meal #2, Time/Location _____
_____
_____
_____

Snack #2, Time/Location _____
_____
_____

Meal #3, Time/Location _____
_____
_____
_____

Snack #3, Time/Location _____
_____
_____

HOW DO YOU FEEL?
(Include Symptom/Time)
_____
_____
_____
_____
_____
_____
_____
_____
_____
_____
_____
_____
_____
_____
_____
_____
_____
_____
_____
_____
_____
_____
_____
_____
_____
_____
_____
_____
_____
_____
_____
_____
_____
_____
_____
_____
_____
_____
_____

EXERCISE: What exercise did you do today? How long? How do you feel?
_____
_____
_____

WATER: Cross off each 8-ounce glass of water you drank today. (Mark other beverages with meals.)

1   2   3   4   5   6   7   8   9   10

LAST NIGHT'S SLEEP

When did you fall asleep last night? _____

When did you wake this morning? _____

How well did you sleep last night? (Rate from 1-10, with 10 being best) _____

Comments about sleep

_____
_____
_____
_____
_____
_____
_____
_____
_____
_____
_____
_____
_____
_____
_____
_____
_____
_____
_____
_____

NEW MEDICATIONS/VITAMINS: List new medications. What side effects did you observe?

_____
_____
_____
_____
_____
_____
_____
_____
_____
_____
_____
_____
_____
_____
_____

VITALS

Blood Sugar/Time _____/_____
Blood Sugar/Time _____/_____

Blood Pressure/Time _____/_____
Blood Pressure/Time _____/_____

Weight _____

BOWEL MOVEMENTS

BM No. 1/Time_____
BM Type (Circle) 1   2   3   4   5   6   7

Observations: _____
_____
_____

BM No. 2/Time_____
BM Type (Circle) 1   2   3   4   5   6   7

Observations: _____
_____
_____

BM No. 3/Time_____
BM Type (Circle) 1   2   3   4   5   6   7

Observations: _____
_____
_____

What challenge did you overcome today?
_____
_____
_____

What are you grateful for?
_____
_____
_____

What's the best thing that happened today?
_____
_____
_____

IT AIN'T JUST THE DIET
FOOD & WELLNESS DAILY LOG

Date: _____ Test Day #_____

Circle your suspected problem foods.
Common allergens: citrus, coffee, corn, dairy, eggs, fish/shellfish, gluten, meat (beef, lamb, pork), peanuts, raw fruits & vegetables, soy, tree nuts

WHAT DID YOU EAT TODAY?

Meal #1, Time/Location _____

_____
_____
_____
_____

Snack #1, Time/Location _____

_____
_____

Meal #2, Time/Location _____

_____
_____
_____
_____

Snack #2, Time/Location _____

_____
_____

Meal #3, Time/Location _____

_____
_____
_____
_____

Snack #3, Time/Location _____

_____
_____

HOW DO YOU FEEL?
(Include Symptom/Time)

_____
_____
_____
_____
_____
_____
_____
_____
_____
_____
_____
_____
_____
_____
_____
_____
_____
_____
_____
_____
_____
_____
_____
_____
_____
_____
_____
_____
_____
_____
_____
_____
_____
_____

EXERCISE: What exercise did you do today? How long? How do you feel?

_____
_____
_____

WATER: Cross off each 8-ounce glass of water you drank today. (Mark other beverages with meals.)

1   2   3   4   5   6   7   8   9   10

LAST NIGHT'S SLEEP

When did you fall asleep last night? _____

When did you wake this morning? _____

How well did you sleep last night? (Rate from 1-10, with 10 being best) _____

Comments about sleep

_____
_____
_____
_____
_____
_____
_____
_____
_____
_____
_____
_____
_____
_____
_____
_____

NEW MEDICATIONS/VITAMINS: List new medications. What side effects did you observe?

_____
_____
_____
_____
_____
_____
_____
_____
_____
_____
_____
_____

VITALS
Blood Sugar/Time _____/_____
Blood Sugar/Time _____/_____

Blood Pressure/Time _____/_____
Blood Pressure/Time _____/_____

Weight _____

BOWEL MOVEMENTS

BM No. 1/Time_____
BM Type (Circle) 1   2   3   4   5   6   7

Observations: _____
_____
_____

BM No. 2/Time_____
BM Type (Circle) 1   2   3   4   5   6   7

Observations: _____
_____
_____

BM No. 3/Time_____
BM Type (Circle) 1   2   3   4   5   6   7

Observations: _____
_____
_____

What challenge did you overcome today?
_____
_____
_____

What are you grateful for?
_____
_____
_____

What's the best thing that happened today?
_____
_____
_____

Food Allergies, Sensitivities, & Intolerances Symptoms Checklist

Week 13 Assessment

Date: _____

Check each symptom you have experienced after eating (currently or in the recent past).

Breathing
- ☐ Sneezing
- ☐ Stuffy nose/sinuses
- ☐ Congestion
- ☐ Runny nose
- ☐ Face pain
- ☐ Difficulty breathing
- ☐ Wheezing or asthma

Skin
- ☐ Hives
- ☐ Eczema or rash
- ☐ Dandruff
- ☐ Ticklishness
- ☐ Flushing
- ☐ Rosy cheeks or ears

Eyes
- ☐ Itchy eyes
- ☐ Dry eyes

Digestive
- ☐ Bloating
- ☐ Gas
- ☐ Constipated
- ☐ Diarrhea or loose stools
- ☐ More bowel movements
- ☐ Fewer bowel movements
- ☐ Abdominal cramping
- ☐ Stinky bowel movements
- ☐ Undigested food in stool
- ☐ Bloody stool

Brain/Thinking
- ☐ Brain fog
- ☐ Inability to concentrate
- ☐ Disjointed or distractible thinking
- ☐ Headaches
- ☐ Glassy-eyed or spacey
- ☐ Trouble remembering things

Energy
- ☐ Hyperactivity
- ☐ Restlessness
- ☐ Tiredness/fatigue
- ☐ Low energy/activity

Difference in Sleep
- ☐ Better
- ☐ Worse
- ☐ Restless leg while sleeping
- ☐ Ideas why? _____

Pain
- ☐ Joint pain
- ☐ Muscle pain
- ☐ Other pain: _____

Mood
- ☐ Ecstatic
- ☐ Happy
- ☐ Neutral
- ☐ Sad
- ☐ Angry/Irritable
- ☐ Calm
- ☐ Anxious
- ☐ Feeling stressed (hair on fire)
- ☐ Filled with creativity
- ☐ Exhausted/no energy

Hunger Changes
- ☐ Craving certain foods (list) _____
- ☐ Hungry all the time
- ☐ Little or no interest in food

Other
- ☐ Bad breath
- ☐ Stinky feet
- ☐ Sweating hands/feet
- ☐ Other: _____

Notes:

_____
_____
_____
_____
_____
_____
_____
_____
_____
_____

Week 13 Journal Prompt

What did you learn? Now that you have nearly completed the log pages, write your overall observations, suspicions, and conclusions below. If you do not think you have found a clear solution to your healthcare worries and issues, please follow up with your healthcare professional to discuss your next steps.

_____
_____
_____
_____
_____
_____
_____
_____
_____
_____
_____
_____
_____
_____
_____
_____
_____
_____
_____
_____
_____
_____
_____
_____
_____
_____
_____
_____
_____
_____
_____

IT AIN'T JUST THE DIET
FOOD & WELLNESS DAILY LOG

Date: _____ Test Day #_____

Circle your suspected problem foods.
Common allergens: citrus, coffee, corn, dairy, eggs, fish/shellfish, gluten, meat (beef, lamb, pork), peanuts, raw fruits & vegetables, soy, tree nuts

WHAT DID YOU EAT TODAY?

Meal #1, Time/Location _____
_____
_____
_____

Snack #1, Time/Location _____
_____
_____

Meal #2, Time/Location _____
_____
_____
_____

Snack #2, Time/Location _____
_____
_____

Meal #3, Time/Location _____
_____
_____
_____

Snack #3, Time/Location _____
_____
_____

HOW DO YOU FEEL?
(Include Symptom/Time)
_____
_____
_____
_____
_____
_____
_____
_____
_____
_____
_____
_____
_____
_____
_____
_____
_____
_____
_____
_____
_____
_____
_____
_____
_____
_____
_____
_____
_____
_____
_____
_____
_____
_____
_____

EXERCISE: What exercise did you do today? How long? How do you feel?
_____
_____
_____

WATER: Cross off each 8-ounce glass of water you drank today. (Mark other beverages with meals.)

1   2   3   4   5   6   7   8   9   10

LAST NIGHT'S SLEEP

When did you fall asleep last night? _____

When did you wake this morning? _____

How well did you sleep last night? (Rate from 1-10, with 10 being best) _____

Comments about sleep

_____
_____
_____
_____
_____
_____
_____
_____
_____
_____
_____
_____
_____
_____
_____
_____
_____
_____

NEW MEDICATIONS/VITAMINS: List new medications. What side effects did you observe?

_____
_____
_____
_____
_____
_____
_____
_____
_____
_____
_____
_____
_____
_____

VITALS

Blood Sugar/Time _____/_____
Blood Sugar/Time _____/_____

Blood Pressure/Time _____/_____
Blood Pressure/Time _____/_____

Weight _____

BOWEL MOVEMENTS

BM No. 1/Time_____
BM Type (Circle) 1   2   3   4   5   6   7

Observations: _____
_____
_____

BM No. 2/Time_____
BM Type (Circle) 1   2   3   4   5   6   7

Observations: _____
_____
_____

BM No. 3/Time_____
BM Type (Circle) 1   2   3   4   5   6   7

Observations: _____
_____
_____

What challenge did you overcome today?

_____
_____
_____

What are you grateful for?

_____
_____
_____

What's the best thing that happened today?

_____
_____
_____

IT AIN'T JUST THE DIET
FOOD & WELLNESS DAILY LOG

Date: _____ Test Day #_____

Circle your suspected problem foods.
Common allergens: citrus, coffee, corn, dairy, eggs, fish/shellfish, gluten, meat (beef, lamb, pork), peanuts, raw fruits & vegetables, soy, tree nuts

WHAT DID YOU EAT TODAY?

Meal #1, Time/Location _____
_____
_____
_____

Snack #1, Time/Location _____
_____

Meal #2, Time/Location _____
_____
_____
_____

Snack #2, Time/Location _____
_____

Meal #3, Time/Location _____
_____
_____
_____

Snack #3, Time/Location _____
_____

HOW DO YOU FEEL?
(Include Symptom/Time)
_____
_____
_____
_____
_____
_____
_____
_____
_____
_____
_____
_____
_____
_____
_____
_____
_____
_____
_____
_____
_____
_____
_____
_____
_____
_____
_____
_____
_____
_____
_____
_____

EXERCISE: What exercise did you do today? How long? How do you feel?
_____
_____

WATER: Cross off each 8-ounce glass of water you drank today. (Mark other beverages with meals.)

1   2   3   4   5   6   7   8   9   10

LAST NIGHT'S SLEEP

When did you fall asleep last night? _____

When did you wake this morning? _____

How well did you sleep last night? (Rate from 1-10, with 10 being best) _____

Comments about sleep

_____
_____
_____
_____
_____
_____
_____
_____
_____
_____
_____
_____
_____
_____
_____
_____
_____
_____
_____
_____

NEW MEDICATIONS/VITAMINS: List new medications. What side effects did you observe?

_____
_____
_____
_____
_____
_____
_____
_____
_____
_____
_____
_____
_____
_____
_____
_____

VITALS

Blood Sugar/Time _____/_____
Blood Sugar/Time _____/_____

Blood Pressure/Time _____/_____
Blood Pressure/Time _____/_____

Weight _____

BOWEL MOVEMENTS

BM No. 1/Time_____

BM Type (Circle) 1   2   3   4   5   6   7

Observations: _____
_____
_____

BM No. 2/Time_____

BM Type (Circle) 1   2   3   4   5   6   7

Observations: _____
_____
_____

BM No. 3/Time_____

BM Type (Circle) 1   2   3   4   5   6   7

Observations: _____
_____
_____

What challenge did you overcome today?

_____
_____
_____

What are you grateful for?

_____
_____
_____

What's the best thing that happened today?

_____
_____
_____

IT AIN'T JUST THE DIET
FOOD & WELLNESS DAILY LOG

Date: _____ Test Day #_____

Circle your suspected problem foods.
Common allergens: citrus, coffee, corn, dairy, eggs, fish/shellfish, gluten, meat (beef, lamb, pork), peanuts, raw fruits & vegetables, soy, tree nuts

WHAT DID YOU EAT TODAY?

Meal #1, Time/Location _____

_____

_____

_____

Snack #1, Time/Location _____

_____

_____

Meal #2, Time/Location _____

_____

_____

_____

Snack #2, Time/Location _____

_____

_____

Meal #3, Time/Location _____

_____

_____

_____

Snack #3, Time/Location _____

_____

_____

HOW DO YOU FEEL?
(Include Symptom/Time)

_____
_____
_____
_____
_____
_____
_____
_____
_____
_____
_____
_____
_____
_____
_____
_____
_____
_____
_____
_____
_____
_____
_____
_____
_____
_____
_____
_____
_____
_____
_____
_____
_____
_____
_____
_____
_____

EXERCISE: What exercise did you do today? How long? How do you feel?

_____
_____
_____

WATER: Cross off each 8-ounce glass of water you drank today. (Mark other beverages with meals.)

1   2   3   4   5   6   7   8   9   10

LAST NIGHT'S SLEEP

When did you fall asleep last night? _____

When did you wake this morning? _____

How well did you sleep last night? (Rate from 1-10, with 10 being best) _____

Comments about sleep

_____
_____
_____
_____
_____
_____
_____
_____
_____
_____
_____
_____
_____
_____
_____
_____
_____
_____
_____

NEW MEDICATIONS/VITAMINS: List new medications. What side effects did you observe?

_____
_____
_____
_____
_____
_____
_____
_____
_____
_____
_____
_____
_____

VITALS

Blood Sugar/Time _____/_____
Blood Sugar/Time _____/_____

Blood Pressure/Time _____/_____
Blood Pressure/Time _____/_____

Weight _____

BOWEL MOVEMENTS

BM No. 1/Time_____
BM Type (Circle) 1   2   3   4   5   6   7

Observations: _____
_____
_____

BM No. 2/Time_____
BM Type (Circle) 1   2   3   4   5   6   7

Observations: _____
_____
_____

BM No. 3/Time_____
BM Type (Circle) 1   2   3   4   5   6   7

Observations: _____
_____
_____

What challenge did you overcome today?

_____
_____
_____

What are you grateful for?

_____
_____
_____

What's the best thing that happened today?

_____
_____
_____

IT AIN'T JUST THE DIET
FOOD & WELLNESS DAILY LOG

Date: _____ Test Day #_____

Circle your suspected problem foods.
Common allergens: citrus, coffee, corn, dairy, eggs, fish/shellfish, gluten, meat (beef, lamb, pork), peanuts, raw fruits & vegetables, soy, tree nuts

WHAT DID YOU EAT TODAY?

Meal #1, Time/Location _____

_____
_____
_____

Snack #1, Time/Location _____

_____
_____

Meal #2, Time/Location _____

_____
_____
_____

Snack #2, Time/Location _____

_____
_____

Meal #3, Time/Location _____

_____
_____
_____

Snack #3, Time/Location _____

_____
_____

EXERCISE: What exercise did you do today? How long? How do you feel?

_____
_____
_____

HOW DO YOU FEEL?
(Include Symptom/Time)

_____
_____
_____
_____
_____
_____
_____
_____
_____
_____
_____
_____
_____
_____
_____
_____
_____
_____
_____
_____
_____
_____
_____
_____
_____
_____
_____
_____
_____
_____
_____
_____
_____
_____

WATER: Cross off each 8-ounce glass of water you drank today. (Mark other beverages with meals.)

1   2   3   4   5   6   7   8   9   10

LAST NIGHT'S SLEEP

When did you fall asleep last night? _____

When did you wake this morning? _____

How well did you sleep last night? (Rate from 1-10, with 10 being best) _____

Comments about sleep

_____
_____
_____
_____
_____
_____
_____
_____
_____
_____
_____
_____
_____
_____
_____
_____
_____
_____
_____

NEW MEDICATIONS/VITAMINS: List new medications. What side effects did you observe?

_____
_____
_____
_____
_____
_____
_____
_____
_____
_____
_____
_____
_____
_____

VITALS

Blood Sugar/Time _____/_____
Blood Sugar/Time _____/_____

Blood Pressure/Time _____/_____
Blood Pressure/Time _____/_____

Weight _____

BOWEL MOVEMENTS

BM No. 1/Time_____
BM Type (Circle) 1   2   3   4   5   6   7

Observations: _____
_____
_____

BM No. 2/Time_____
BM Type (Circle) 1   2   3   4   5   6   7

Observations: _____
_____
_____

BM No. 3/Time_____
BM Type (Circle) 1   2   3   4   5   6   7

Observations: _____
_____
_____

What challenge did you overcome today?
_____
_____
_____

What are you grateful for?
_____
_____
_____

What's the best thing that happened today?
_____
_____
_____

IT AIN'T JUST THE DIET
FOOD & WELLNESS DAILY LOG

Date: _____ Test Day #_____

Circle your suspected problem foods.
Common allergens: citrus, coffee, corn, dairy, eggs, fish/shellfish, gluten, meat (beef, lamb, pork), peanuts, raw fruits & vegetables, soy, tree nuts

WHAT DID YOU EAT TODAY?

Meal #1, Time/Location _____
_____
_____
_____

Snack #1, Time/Location _____
_____
_____

Meal #2, Time/Location _____
_____
_____
_____

Snack #2, Time/Location _____
_____
_____

Meal #3, Time/Location _____
_____
_____
_____

Snack #3, Time/Location _____
_____
_____

HOW DO YOU FEEL?
(Include Symptom/Time)
_____
_____
_____
_____
_____
_____
_____
_____
_____
_____
_____
_____
_____
_____
_____
_____
_____
_____
_____
_____
_____
_____
_____
_____
_____
_____
_____
_____
_____
_____
_____
_____
_____
_____
_____
_____
_____

EXERCISE: What exercise did you do today? How long? How do you feel?
_____
_____
_____

WATER: Cross off each 8-ounce glass of water you drank today. (Mark other beverages with meals.)

1   2   3   4   5   6   7   8   9   10

LAST NIGHT'S SLEEP

When did you fall asleep last night? _____

When did you wake this morning? _____

How well did you sleep last night? (Rate from 1-10, with 10 being best) _____

Comments about sleep

_____
_____
_____
_____
_____
_____
_____
_____
_____
_____
_____
_____
_____
_____
_____
_____
_____
_____

NEW MEDICATIONS/VITAMINS: List new medications. What side effects did you observe?

_____
_____
_____
_____
_____
_____
_____
_____
_____
_____
_____
_____
_____
_____
_____

VITALS

Blood Sugar/Time _____/_____
Blood Sugar/Time _____/_____

Blood Pressure/Time _____/_____
Blood Pressure/Time _____/_____

Weight _____

BOWEL MOVEMENTS

BM No. 1/Time_____
BM Type (Circle) 1   2   3   4   5   6   7

Observations: _____
_____
_____

BM No. 2/Time_____
BM Type (Circle) 1   2   3   4   5   6   7

Observations: _____
_____
_____

BM No. 3/Time_____
BM Type (Circle) 1   2   3   4   5   6   7

Observations: _____
_____
_____

What challenge did you overcome today?
_____
_____
_____
_____

What are you grateful for?
_____
_____
_____
_____

What's the best thing that happened today?
_____
_____
_____
_____

IT AIN'T JUST THE DIET
FOOD & WELLNESS DAILY LOG

Date: _____ Test Day #_____

Circle your suspected problem foods.
Common allergens: citrus, coffee, corn, dairy, eggs, fish/shellfish, gluten, meat (beef, lamb, pork), peanuts, raw fruits & vegetables, soy, tree nuts

WHAT DID YOU EAT TODAY?

Meal #1, Time/Location _____
_____
_____
_____

Snack #1, Time/Location _____
_____
_____

Meal #2, Time/Location _____
_____
_____
_____

Snack #2, Time/Location _____
_____
_____

Meal #3, Time/Location _____
_____
_____
_____

Snack #3, Time/Location _____
_____

HOW DO YOU FEEL?
(Include Symptom/Time)
_____
_____
_____
_____
_____
_____
_____
_____
_____
_____
_____
_____
_____
_____
_____
_____
_____
_____
_____
_____
_____
_____
_____
_____
_____
_____
_____
_____
_____
_____
_____
_____

EXERCISE: What exercise did you do today? How long? How do you feel?
_____
_____
_____

WATER: Cross off each 8-ounce glass of water you drank today. (Mark other beverages with meals.)

1   2   3   4   5   6   7   8   9   10

LAST NIGHT'S SLEEP

When did you fall asleep last night? _____

When did you wake this morning? _____

How well did you sleep last night? (Rate from 1-10, with 10 being best) _____

Comments about sleep

_____
_____
_____
_____
_____
_____
_____
_____
_____
_____
_____
_____
_____
_____
_____
_____
_____
_____

NEW MEDICATIONS/VITAMINS: List new medications. What side effects did you observe?

_____
_____
_____
_____
_____
_____
_____
_____
_____
_____
_____
_____
_____

VITALS

Blood Sugar/Time _____/_____
Blood Sugar/Time _____/_____

Blood Pressure/Time _____/_____
Blood Pressure/Time _____/_____

Weight _____

BOWEL MOVEMENTS

BM No. 1/Time_____
BM Type (Circle) 1   2   3   4   5   6   7

Observations: _____
_____
_____

BM No. 2/Time_____
BM Type (Circle) 1   2   3   4   5   6   7

Observations: _____
_____
_____

BM No. 3/Time_____
BM Type (Circle) 1   2   3   4   5   6   7

Observations: _____
_____
_____

What challenge did you overcome today?
_____
_____
_____

What are you grateful for?
_____
_____
_____

What's the best thing that happened today?
_____
_____
_____

IT AIN'T JUST THE DIET
FOOD & WELLNESS DAILY LOG

Date: _____ Test Day #_____

Circle your suspected problem foods.
Common allergens: citrus, coffee, corn, dairy, eggs, fish/shellfish, gluten, meat (beef, lamb, pork), peanuts, raw fruits & vegetables, soy, tree nuts

WHAT DID YOU EAT TODAY?

Meal #1, Time/Location _____
_____
_____
_____

Snack #1, Time/Location _____
_____

Meal #2, Time/Location _____
_____
_____
_____

Snack #2, Time/Location _____
_____

Meal #3, Time/Location _____
_____
_____
_____

Snack #3, Time/Location _____
_____
_____

HOW DO YOU FEEL?
(Include Symptom/Time)
_____
_____
_____
_____
_____
_____
_____
_____
_____
_____
_____
_____
_____
_____
_____
_____
_____
_____
_____
_____
_____
_____
_____
_____
_____
_____
_____
_____

EXERCISE: What exercise did you do today? How long? How do you feel?
_____
_____
_____

WATER: Cross off each 8-ounce glass of water you drank today. (Mark other beverages with meals.)

1   2   3   4   5   6   7   8   9   10

LAST NIGHT'S SLEEP

When did you fall asleep last night? _____

When did you wake this morning? _____

How well did you sleep last night? (Rate from 1-10, with 10 being best) _____

Comments about sleep

_____
_____
_____
_____
_____
_____
_____
_____
_____
_____
_____
_____
_____
_____
_____
_____
_____
_____
_____

NEW MEDICATIONS/VITAMINS: List new medications. What side effects did you observe?

_____
_____
_____
_____
_____
_____
_____
_____
_____
_____
_____
_____
_____
_____

VITALS

Blood Sugar/Time _____/_____
Blood Sugar/Time _____/_____

Blood Pressure/Time _____/_____
Blood Pressure/Time _____/_____

Weight _____

BOWEL MOVEMENTS

BM No. 1/Time_____
BM Type (Circle) 1   2   3   4   5   6   7

Observations: _____
_____
_____

BM No. 2/Time_____
BM Type (Circle) 1   2   3   4   5   6   7

Observations: _____
_____
_____

BM No. 3/Time_____
BM Type (Circle) 1   2   3   4   5   6   7

Observations: _____
_____
_____

What challenge did you overcome today?
_____
_____
_____
_____

What are you grateful for?
_____
_____
_____
_____

What's the best thing that happened today?
_____
_____
_____
_____

IT AIN'T JUST THE DIET
FOOD & WELLNESS DAILY LOG

Date: _____ Test Day #_____

Circle your suspected problem foods.
Common allergens: citrus, coffee, corn, dairy, eggs, fish/shellfish, gluten, meat (beef, lamb, pork), peanuts, raw fruits & vegetables, soy, tree nuts

WHAT DID YOU EAT TODAY?

Meal #1, Time/Location _____
_____
_____
_____

Snack #1, Time/Location _____
_____
_____

Meal #2, Time/Location _____
_____
_____
_____

Snack #2, Time/Location _____
_____
_____

Meal #3, Time/Location _____
_____
_____
_____

Snack #3, Time/Location _____
_____
_____

HOW DO YOU FEEL?
(Include Symptom/Time)
_____
_____
_____
_____
_____
_____
_____
_____
_____
_____
_____
_____
_____
_____
_____
_____
_____
_____
_____
_____
_____
_____
_____
_____
_____
_____
_____
_____
_____
_____
_____
_____
_____
_____
_____
_____
_____
_____

EXERCISE: What exercise did you do today? How long? How do you feel?
_____
_____
_____

WATER: Cross off each 8-ounce glass of water you drank today. (Mark other beverages with meals.)

1   2   3   4   5   6   7   8   9   10

LAST NIGHT'S SLEEP

When did you fall asleep last night? _____

When did you wake this morning? _____

How well did you sleep last night? (Rate from 1-10, with 10 being best) _____

Comments about sleep

_____
_____
_____
_____
_____
_____
_____
_____
_____
_____
_____
_____
_____
_____
_____
_____
_____
_____
_____

NEW MEDICATIONS/VITAMINS: List new medications. What side effects did you observe?

_____
_____
_____
_____
_____
_____
_____
_____
_____
_____
_____
_____
_____
_____
_____
_____

VITALS

Blood Sugar/Time _____/_____
Blood Sugar/Time _____/_____

Blood Pressure/Time _____/_____
Blood Pressure/Time _____/_____

Weight _____

BOWEL MOVEMENTS

BM No. 1/Time_____
BM Type (Circle) 1   2   3   4   5   6   7

Observations: _____
_____
_____

BM No. 2/Time_____
BM Type (Circle) 1   2   3   4   5   6   7

Observations: _____
_____
_____

BM No. 3/Time_____
BM Type (Circle) 1   2   3   4   5   6   7

Observations: _____
_____
_____

What challenge did you overcome today?
_____
_____
_____

What are you grateful for?
_____
_____
_____

What's the best thing that happened today?
_____
_____
_____

Food Allergies, Sensitivities, & Intolerances Symptoms Checklist

Final Assessment

Date: _____

Check each symptom you have experienced after eating (currently or in the recent past).

Breathing
- ☐ Sneezing
- ☐ Stuffy nose/sinuses
- ☐ Congestion
- ☐ Runny nose
- ☐ Face pain
- ☐ Difficulty breathing
- ☐ Wheezing or asthma

Skin
- ☐ Hives
- ☐ Eczema or rash
- ☐ Dandruff
- ☐ Ticklishness
- ☐ Flushing
- ☐ Rosy cheeks or ears

Eyes
- ☐ Itchy eyes
- ☐ Dry eyes

Digestive
- ☐ Bloating
- ☐ Gas
- ☐ Constipated
- ☐ Diarrhea or loose stools
- ☐ More bowel movements
- ☐ Fewer bowel movements
- ☐ Abdominal cramping
- ☐ Stinky bowel movements
- ☐ Undigested food in stool
- ☐ Bloody stool

Brain/Thinking
- ☐ Brain fog
- ☐ Inability to concentrate
- ☐ Disjointed or distractible thinking
- ☐ Headaches
- ☐ Glassy-eyed or spacey
- ☐ Trouble remembering things

Energy
- ☐ Hyperactivity
- ☐ Restlessness
- ☐ Tiredness/fatigue
- ☐ Low energy/activity

Difference in Sleep
- ☐ Better
- ☐ Worse
- ☐ Restless leg while sleeping
- ☐ Ideas why? _____

Pain
- ☐ Joint pain
- ☐ Muscle pain
- ☐ Other pain: _____

Mood
- ☐ Ecstatic
- ☐ Happy
- ☐ Neutral
- ☐ Sad
- ☐ Angry/Irritable
- ☐ Calm
- ☐ Anxious
- ☐ Feeling stressed (hair on fire)
- ☐ Filled with creativity
- ☐ Exhausted/no energy

Hunger Changes
- ☐ Craving certain foods (list) _____
- ☐ Hungry all the time
- ☐ Little or no interest in food

Other
- ☐ Bad breath
- ☐ Stinky feet
- ☐ Sweating hands/feet
- ☐ Other: _____

Notes:

_____
_____
_____
_____
_____
_____
_____
_____
_____
_____
_____

What Are Your Next Steps?

_____
_____
_____
_____
_____
_____
_____
_____
_____
_____
_____
_____
_____
_____
_____
_____
_____
_____
_____
_____
_____
_____
_____
_____
_____
_____
_____
_____
_____
_____
_____
_____
_____
_____
_____
_____

Notes:

ENDNOTES

1   Ruchi S. Gupta, M.D., MPH, et. al., JAMA Network Open, "Prevalence and Severity of Food Allergies Among US Adults," https://www.ncbi.nlm.nih.gov/pmc/articles/PMC6324316/, January 4, 2019.

2   Terry Wahls, M.D., with Eve Adamson, The Wahls Protocol, A Radical New Way to Treat All Chronic Autoimmune Conditions Using Paleo Principles, Avery an imprint of Penguin Random House LLC, New York, 2014, 2020, pages 108, 134-135.

3   Kimberly Goad, WebMD, "Food Allergy Myths and Facts," https://www.webmd.com/allergies/features/food-allergy-myths#1, February 1, 2016.

4   Doris Rapp, M.D., Is This Your Child? Discovering and Treating Unrecognized Allergies in Children and Adults, William Morrow & Co., New York, 1991, pages 59-60.

5   "Food Allergy Essentials: Common Allergens," Food Allergy Research and Education (FARE), McLean, Virginia, June 4, 2020, https://www.foodallergy.org/living-food-allergies/food-allergy-essentials/common-allergens.

6   What You Need to Know about Food Allergies," US Food & Drug Administration, https://www.fda.gov/food/buy-store-serve-safe-food/food-allergies-what-you-need-know, accessed March 23, 2021.

7   Doris Rapp, M.D., Is This Your Child? Discovering and Treating Unrecognized Allergies in Children and Adults, William Morrow & Co., New York, 1991, page 188.

8   Doris Rapp, M.D., Is This Your Child? Discovering and Treating Unrecognized Allergies in Children and Adults, William Morrow & Co., New York, 1991, page 187.

9   Nayana Ambardekar (reviewed by), WebMD, "What are symptoms of severe allergy?", July 7, 2018, https://www.webmd.com/allergies/qa/what-are-symptoms-of-severe-allergy.

10 Doris Rapp, M.D., Is This Your Child? Discovering and Treating Unrecognized Allergies in Children and Adults, William Morrow & Co., New York, 1991, page 188.

11 Doris Rapp, M.D., Is This Your Child? Discovering and Treating Unrecognized Allergies in Children and Adults, William Morrow & Co., New York, 1991, page 63.

12 Dr. Kenneth Heaton, 1936–2013, University of Bristol, Bristol, U.K., http://www.bristol.ac.uk/news/2013/9601.html, accessed September 11, 2020.

13 Carol DerSarkissian (reviewed by), "What Kind of Poop Do I Have?," WebMD, January 16, 2020, https://www.webmd.com/digestive-disorders/poop-chart-bristol-stool-scale.

14 Distributed with kind permission of Dr. K. W. Heaton, formerly Reader in Medicine at the University of Bristol. Reproduced as a service to the medical profession by Norgine Ltd. ©2017 Norgine group of companies.

15 Carol DerSarkissian (reviewed by), "What Kind of Poop Do I Have?," WebMD, January 16, 2020, https://www.webmd.com/digestive-disorders/poop-chart-bristol-stool-scale.

16 Kris Shaw, "Why Do We Often Crave The Foods We Are Allergic To?," Seattle Allergy Natural Solutions, Seattle, Washington, May 11, 2019, https://seattleallergynaturalsolutions.com/why-do-we-often-crave-foods-we-are-allergic-to/.

17 Doris Rapp, M.D., Is This Your Child? Discovering and Treating Unrecognized Allergies in Children and Adults, William Morrow & Co., New York, 1991, pages 59-60.

RECOMMENDED RESOURCES

Books

Feed Your Kids Right, Dr. Smith's Program for Your Child's Total Health, Smith, Lendon H., M.D., Dell Publishing Company (part of Penguin Random House Publishing), 1980. This is a legacy book that strongly influenced how I fed my daughter. I recommend you read it. It is no longer available for sale.

Is This Your Child? Discovering and Treating Unrecognized Allergies in Children and Adults, Rapp, Doris, M.D., New York: William Morrow & Co., 1991.

Jennifer's Way, Esposito, Jennifer with Eve Adamson, Da Capo Press, a member of Perseus Books Group, New York, 2014, 2015.

The Wahls Protocol, A Radical New Way to Treat All Chronic Autoimmune Conditions Using Paleo Principles, Wahls, Terry M.D., with Eve Adamson, Avery an imprint of Penguin Random House LLC, New York, 2014, 2020.

GLOSSARY

Anaphylactic shock | Extreme, often life-threatening allergic reaction to an antigen to which the body has become hypersensitive.

Antihistamine | A drug or other compound that inhibits the physiological effects of histamine, used especially in the treatment of allergies.

Bristol Stool Form Scale (Chart) | A diagnostic medical tool designed to classify the form of human feces into seven categories.

Constipation/Constipated | Generally described as having fewer than three bowel movements a week.

Diarrhea | Condition in which feces are discharged from the bowels frequently and in a liquid form.

FARE (Food Allergy Research and Education) | The world's largest non-profit organization dedicated to food allergy awareness, education, research, and advocacy; the group provides information, programs, and resources about food allergies and anaphylaxis.

Food Allergy | Reactions to food that prompt your immune system to go into high alert when you eat a particular food or category of food.

Food Intolerance | Food reactions that do not directly involve your immune system. Generally, a food intolerance is due to the inability to process or digest a food and it manifests itself entirely in the digestive system.

Food Sensitivity | Reactions to food that involve the immune system, but the symptoms are delayed and often harder to figure out than allergies.

Perimenopause or "around menopause" | Refers to the time during which a woman's body makes the natural transition to menopause, marking the end of the reproductive years.

Made in the USA
Middletown, DE
30 April 2021